D0433782

SCOTTISH COUNTRY BUSINESS REFERENCE BOOK

1991

Publisher
Bruce Ford

GB Ford Associates,
7 Rosebery Crescent,
Edinburgh, EH12 5JP
Tel: 031-346-0549 or 031-337-2271
Fax: 031-337-5881

Editor: Doreen Graham
Printed by Charles Letts (Scotland) Limited,
Thornybank Industrial Estate,
Dalkeith, Midlothian, EH22 2NE

ISBN 1-872326-05-6

British Library Cataloguing in Publication Data
Scottish country business reference book, 1991
1. Scotland. Rural industries and trades.
338.4'768'09411

ISBN 1-872326-05-6

'We have tried where possible to include as many relevant names, addresses, details and practical information, pertaining to the rural sector in Scotland, which can be of use to those operating within this area. If there have been omissions also considered to be important, we apologise and respectfully suggest that any material falling into this category is forwarded to the Publisher, and will be taken into account in advance of the 1992 edition of Scottish Country Business Reference Book.'

CONTENTS

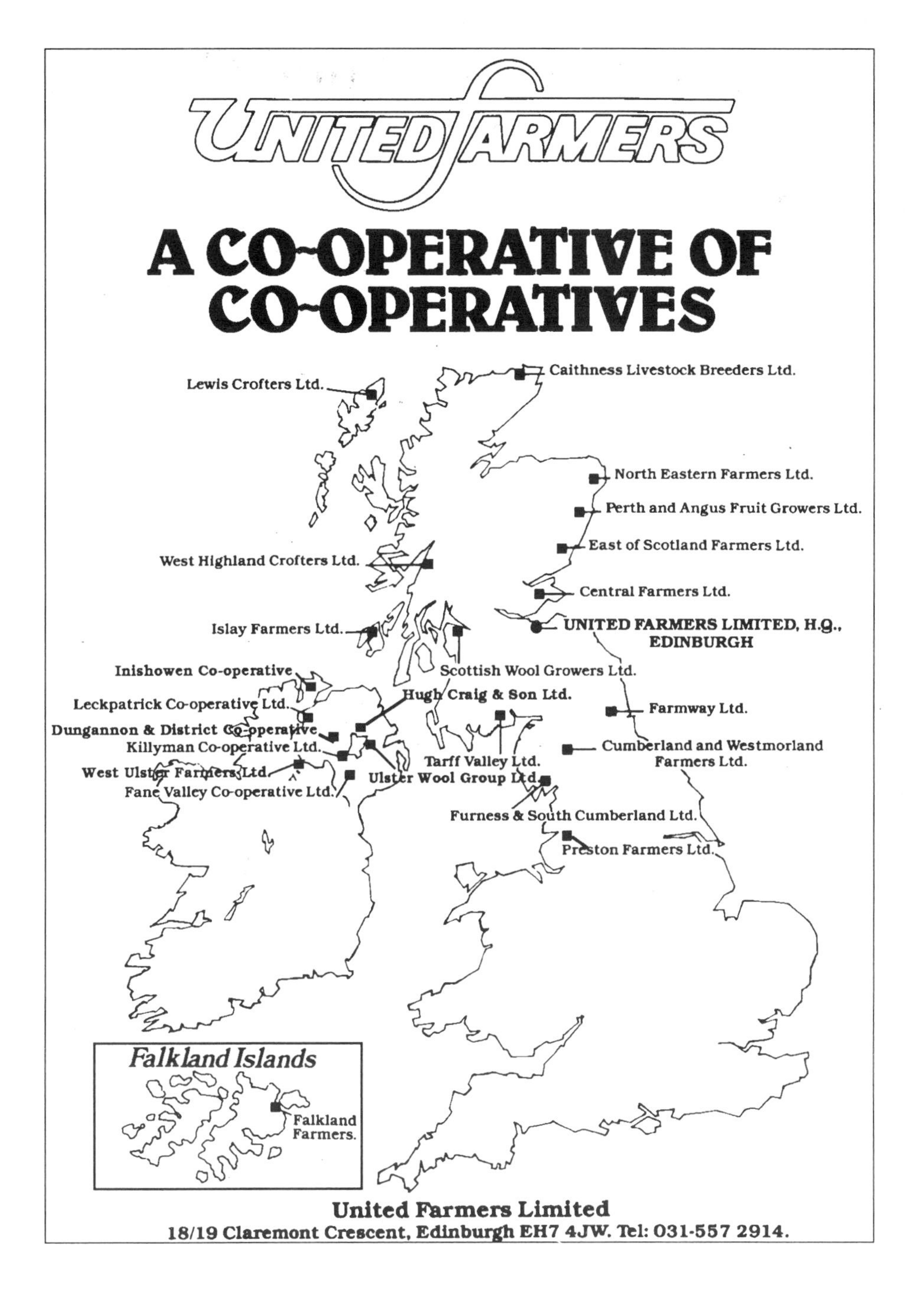

UNITED FARMERS
A CO-OPERATIVE OF CO-OPERATIVES
Caithness Livestock Breeders Ltd.
Lewis Crofters Ltd.
North Eastern Farmers Ltd.
Perth and Angus Fruit Growers Ltd.
East of Scotland Farmers Ltd.
West Highland Crofters Ltd.
Central Farmers Ltd.
Islay Farmers Ltd.
UNITED FARMERS LIMITED, H.Q., EDINBURGH
Scottish Wool Growers Ltd.
Inishowen Co-operative
Hugh Craig & Son Ltd.
Leckpatrick Co-operative Ltd.
Farmway Ltd.
Dungannon & District Co-operative
Killyman Co-operative Ltd.
Cumberland and Westmorland Farmers Ltd.
Tarff Valley Ltd.
West Ulster Farmers Ltd.
Ulster Wool Group Ltd.
Fane Valley Co-operative Ltd.
Furness & South Cumberland Ltd.
Preston Farmers Ltd.
Falkland Islands
Falkland Farmers.
United Farmers Limited
18/19 Claremont Crescent, Edinburgh EH7 4JW. Tel: 031-557 2914.

FOREWORD

IT IS A GREAT PLEASURE to be invited to contribute a Foreword to this second edition of The Scottish Country Business Reference Book in my capacity as chairman-designate of the independent Nature Conservancy Council in Scotland, and of the forthcoming new Scottish Natural Heritage.

Nowadays the talk is of 'greening': greening our cities, greening our countryside. Here in Scotland we start off with a huge advantage, in that Scotland is still a particularly 'green place', from one point of view at least: we have much more countryside left than England. Scotland has about one third of Britain's land area, but only about 10% of the population. It means that Scotland's landowners bear a significant responsibility for huge reaches of our country.

From time immemorial, farming has been the principal land use in Scotland's magnificent countryside. It has never been an easy life. Over 70% of our farmland consists of unimproved rough grazing in the hill areas; this is what makes Scotland so distinctive a part of Britain. Our uplands contain an immensely significant wildlife reserve.

It means that as well as their role in husbandry of the land in supplying Scotland's larder (and our farmers produce enough temperate foodstuffs to supply all our population), our farmers also have a critical role to play in husbanding our natural heritage.

To me, farming and forestry and landowning and nature conservation should be essentially complementary activities. farmers and foresters are the face-workers at the seams of our natural resources held by owners of the land. Their impact on the land is inevitably enormous. To ensure that this impact is ultimately benign, our countryside has to be planned and tended. It means encouraging all those with an interest in the land to become front-line conservationists, with the use of adequate payments to ensure that work in the field is duly rewarded.

Conservation must never become a luxury that only the rich can afford; it must be woven firmly into the fabric of all our economic and social planning.

I believe that the political will is there. I have high hopes that the means will be made available as well. I want to see conservation recognised as an essential factor in all land-use policy measures.

We all share the aim of 'the sustainable use of renewable natural resources', to quote the celebrated dictum from the World Conservation Strategy. By 'natural resources' we must include the most important resource of all – the people of the local communities in our rural areas. It is only through them and their knowledge of the land, their love of the land, their care for the land, that we will ever achieve that aim, of husbanding our heritage properly together for the future as well as the present.

Magnus Magnusson

Magnus Magnusson, K.B.E.

INTRODUCTION

FOLLOWING THE SUCCESSFUL introduction last year of *Scottish Country Business Reference Book*, we have made some changes and improvements to the 1991 edition.

The Book has proved to be a welcome and unique all-round information facility for many actively involved throughout or associated with the rural sector in Scotland. In this ever-changing environment, it is necessary to ensure continuity and efficiency, and vital that where possible the means are at our disposal to assist us in achieving and maintaining such. *Scottish Country Business Reference Book* has now established itself as an invaluable tool on a day-today basis in that respect.

I would personally like to thank the representative and advisory Organisations, and all contributors to this edition. We hope that it positively assists those associated with the countryside seeking success and harmony during 1991.

PUBLISHER

THE NATIONAL FARMERS' UNION OF SCOTLAND

WORKING FOR FARMERS

Democratically organised pressure groups are an essential part of modern society. Minority groups must be organised, otherwise their voice will go unheeded and unheard.

The Scottish NFU strives to protect the total interests of Scotland's primary producers. The Union belongs to its members and it gives them a highly informed, effective political voice, able to act swiftly on their behalf.

Developments in the economics of food production, the inclusion of agriculture in crucial international trade negotiations, and shifts in our political, social and economic environment mean that the industry needs Union to represent the interests of farmers.

The world is changing. It is not the purpose of the NFU to reverse the tide of history. What the Union is striving for is change in a co-ordinated and intelligent way to ensure the maintenance of a productive industry in Scotland's countryside and to retain it as one in which the nation may take pride.

Unity and a sense of purpose are essential. Less than a third of Scotland's MPs represent constituencies which have any significant rural vote. And for every Scottish farmer, there are 450 others elsewhere in the EC.

Despite this the Union has direct access to Government at every level in the UK and because we have our place by right in COPA, we give Scottish farmers, growers, crofters and fish farmers direct access through their Union to the EC Commission and to the European Parliament.

Through their organisation Union members have shorter lines of communication to the decision-making centres, and more direct and immediate access to them, than producers anywhere else in Europe.

The Scottish NFU is a pressure group.

How does the Union operate?

By aiming its activities directly at Ministers and Government officials who make, or advise on policy decisions affecting agriculture.

For example:
- Occasional meetings with the Prime Minister.
- Regular meetings with Agriculture Ministers.
- Regular meetings with Government officials.
- Meetings with EC Commissioners and Commission officials.
- Lobbying MPs, MEPS, Westminster and the European Parliament, and political parties.
- Meetings with regional authorities.

By developing and advocating suitable and necessary policies for agriculture.

For example:
- Beef Premium Scheme 1974.
- Less Favoured Areas Directive 1975.
- EEC sheep regime 1980.
- Introduction of milk quota system 1983/84.

- Agricultural Development Programme 1986/87.
- Arable set aside 1987/88.
- Farm Woodland Scheme 1988.
- Support arrangements for seed potatoes 1 988/89.

By using the knowledge and expertise of the industry itself, of its elected leaders, and of expert staff to advise on administration in implementing and administering schemes for the industry.

For example:
- Suckler Cow Premium Scheme 1980.
- Annual Ewe Premium 1980.
- Weather Aid 1985.
- Chernobyl Compensation Scheme 1987.
- £40m Agricultural Development Programme.
- Landlord/Tenant Milk Quota Division 1986.
- Advocacy of a Rural Development Programme 1988.

By proposing new legislation and necessary changes to existing legislation when and where the need exists, and by ensuring that the industry's interests are taken into account when new legislation is proposed.

For example:

Sites of Special Scientific Interest
Promoting review of operation of Wildlife and Countryside Act 1981 to protect interests of both farmers within designated SSSI's and also those adjacent to such sites.

Planning
Secured relaxation of National Planning Guidelines to permit development on agricultural land.

Tax
Annual submission to Chancellor of the Exchequer with a wide range of Budget recommendations of importance to farmers.

Liability for animals
Instrumental in securing the passage of the Animals (Scotland) Act 1987 modernising the law on civil liability for animals.

Agricultural Holdings Legislation
Secured the passage of the Agricultural Holdings (Amendment) (Scotland) Act 1983 which did away with 'key money' and resulted in a moderation in farm rent increases.

Agriculture Act 1986
Fought for principle of tenants' compensation for milk quotas and dramatically improved terms for tenants better in Scotland than elsewhere in Great Britain.

Firearms Act 1988
Ensured that agriculture's interests were recognised.

Farmland and Rural Development Act 1988
Secured enhanced rates for farm woodlands and diversification.

Food and Environment Protection Act 1988
Regular consultation on Statutory Instruments governing use of agro-chemicals.

Glen Glova Raspberry Replanting Grant Scheme 1988

By acting as the industry's spokesman in public discussion of industry and general economic affairs.

For example:
Press releases.
Publicity leaflets.
Media interviews.
Active membership of the CBI.
Active membership of the Scottish Council Development and Industry.

By ensuring that Scottish farmers represent Scottish agriculture in all significant discussion of agriculture – in Scotland, in the UK and in the EC.

For example:
Membership of COPA (the organisation uniting Europe's farmers' unions).
Membership of International Federation of Agricultural Producers.

And direct interest in and involvement with the work, for example, of:
MLC.
HGCA.
Milk Boards.
Potato Board.
Wool Board.
HIDB.
SDA.
COSLA.
SAC.
Crofters' Commission.
Nature Conservancy Council.
Countryside Commission.
Crown Estate Commissioners.
River Purification Boards.
Local authorities.
Merchants, feed manufacturers, vets and plant breeders' associations, etc.

NATIONAL FARMERS' UNION OF SCOTLAND

Headquarters
17 Grosvenor Crescent, Edinburgh, EH12 5EN.
Tel. 031-337-4333 Fax 031-337-4127
Telex 727672

President
J.A. Ross, Low Auchenree, Portpatrick, Stranraer, Wigtownshire, DG9 8TN.

Vice-Presidents
M. Mackie, Jnr., Westertown, Farm, Rothienorman, Inverurie, Aberdeenshire, AB5 8US.
G.A. Mole, Greenburn, Reston, Eyemouth, Berwickshire TD14 5LP.

Honorary Presidents
J.L. Goodfellow, Cairnton House, Arbroath, Angus, DD11 5SU.
I.D. Grant, CBE, F.R.Ag.S., Thorn, Alyth, Blairgowrie, Perthshire, PH11 8NP.
I.D. Wilson, Drum Farm, Beeswing, Dumfries, DG2 8PB.

Chief Executive
D. Scott Johnston, O.B.E., B.A., Fr.Ag.S.

Director General and Deputy Chief Executive
Robert I. Sandilands, M.A.

Commodity Directors
Tom J. Brady, M.A.
D. Ronnie H. Crichton, A.C.I.S.
Richard G. Henton, B.A.
Caroline J. Lang.

Chief Legal Adviser
Ian A. Melrose, LL.B.

Manager, Business Services Division
Bill Romanis.

Development Manager
Steve H. Anderson, A.C.B.S.I.

Assistant Development Manager
Fred Bauer

Office Manager
Alan S. Wilson.

AREA SECRETARIES

Aberdeen & Kincardine Area
W. Pirie, Thainstone Agricultural Centre, Inverurie, Aberdeenshire, AB5 9NT.
Tel. 0467-25426

Angus Area
G.C. Anderson, NFU Office, 83 North Street, Forfar, Angus, DD8 3BL.
Tel. 0307-63785

Argyll Area (Mid)
T.H. Baney, Orchy Bheag, Dalmally, Argyll, PA33 1AX.
Tel. 083-82-483

Argyll Area (North)
T.H. Baney, Orchy Bheag, Dalmally, Argyll, PA33 1AX.
Tel. 083-82-483

Arran Area (interim)
Mrs. M. Currie, Birchburn, Shiskine, Brodick, Isle of Arran, KA27 8EP.
Tel. 077086-221

Ayr Area
H. Jefferson, NFU Office, County Auction Mart, Castlehill Road, Ayr, KA7 2HT.
Tel. 0292-267801 and 263313

Banff Area
A.A. Meldrum, NFU Office, 193 Mid Street, Keith, Banffshire, AB5 3BQ.
Tel. 054-22-2884

Black Isle and Mid Ross Area
R.C.F. High, NFU Office, 2 Mayfield, High Street, Dingwall, Ross-shire.
Tel. 0349-62430

Borders Area
R.R. Noble, NFU Office, 9 Currie Street, Duns, Berwickshire, TD11 3DL.
Tel. 0361-82291

Bute Area
A. Murray, 43 Crichton Road, Rothesay, Isle of Bute, PA20 9JT.
Tel. 0700-2197

Caithness Area
A. Campbell, NFU Office, 55 Scapa House, Thurso, Caithness, KW14 7JX.
Tel. 0847-65005

Cowal Area
T.H. Baney, Orchy Bheag, Dalmally, Argyll, PA33 1AX.
Tel. 083-82-483

Dumfries and Stewartry Area
J. Milby, NFU Office, 48 Whitesands, Dumfries, DG1 2RS.
Tel. 0387-54270

Easter Ross Area
R.C.F. High, NFU Office, 2 Mayfield, High Street, Dingwall, Ross-shire.
Tel. 0349-62430

Fife and Kinross Area
J. Quigley, NFU Office, Drum Road, Cupar, Fife, KY15 5DU.
Tel. 0334-52594

Forth Valley Area
Mrs E. R. Middleton, Halls of Airth Cottages, Bothkennar, Falkirk, Stirlingshire, FK2 8PN.
Tel. 032-483-531

Inverclyde Area
Miss M.T. Fisher, NFU Office, 134c Main Street, Alexandria, Dunbartonshire, G83 0NZ.
Tel. 0389-55250

Inverness Area
R.C.F. High, NFU Office, 2 Mayfield, High Street, Dingwall, Ross-shire.
Tel. 0349-62430

Islay, Jura, Colonsay and Gigha Area
G.C. Graham, Islay Farmers Ltd., Bowmore, Isle of Islay, PA43 7LJ.
Tel. 049-681-491/2

Kintyre Area
Mrs A. Martin, NFU Office, Glengyle, Campbeltown, Argyll, PA28 6LF.
Tel. 0586-52428

Lanark Area
A.L. Bell, NFU Office, 43 High Street, Lanark, ML11 7LU.
Tel. 0555-2271

Lothians Area
R.G. Allan, NFU Office, Sherwood Works, Eastfield Industrial Estate, Penicuik, EH26 8HA.
Tel. 0968-77160

Moray and Nairn Area
R.F. Anderson, NFU Office, 26 Hay Street, Elgin, IV30 1NQ.
Tel. 0343-542860

Orkney Area
G.S. Burgher, NFU Office, 60 Junction Road, Kirkwall, Orkney, KW15 1AR.
Tel. 0856-2048

Perth Area
J. MacNeill, NFU Office, 28 York Place, Perth, PH2 8EH.
Tel. 0738-25921

Shetland Area
Mrs E.I. Sinclair, 'Goinja Virda', Fladdabister, Shetland, ZE2 9HA.
Tel. 095-03-283

Sutherland Area
I. Thomson, NFU Office, 55 Scapa House, Thurso, Caithness, KW14 7JX.
Tel. 0847-65005

Wigtown Area
I.J.D. Macpherson, NFU Office, Edinburgh Rd, Stranraer, Wigtownshire, DG9 7HH.
Tel. 0776-2964

THE SCOTTISH LANDOWNERS' FEDERATION

WORKING FOR THOSE WHO OWN THE LAND

The Scottish Landowners' Federation is the only organisation representing the interests of rural landowners in Scotland. It was founded in 1906 to represent the interests of landlords at a time when more than 90% of agricultural land was let to tenants.

Since then, there has been a dramatic reduction in the proportion of farm land that is let, but over 80 years on, the Federation has a crucial role to play in protecting and promoting the interests of Scotland's landowners. At a time of such change in the countryside due to the economic and political pressures exerted by an amalgam of Government, the EEC, the 'Green' lobby and a public increasingly demanding more access to Scotland's rural areas, it is essential that Scotland's landowners have a strong and powerful voice.

The more support the Federation has, the more powerful and effective it will be.

The SLF is officially recognised by Government as the representative body on all matters relating to land ownership, a subject that can present complex problems of taxation, the law, insurance, valuation, finance, planning, access and diversification, to name but a few.

The Federation's 4,000 members have access to free advisory and consultancy services on a whole range of businesses and circumstances.

Membership covers all categories of owners of rural land from those with small holdings through to farms, estates, local authorities and corporate bodies.

The Federation maintains a close working relationship with other major organisations concerned with Scotland's rural areas, among them the National Farmers' Union of Scotland. The two organisations regularly liaise on a range of subjects – milk quotas, valuations, landlord/tenant legislation, industry public relations – and although both bodies have distinct roles to play, both share the view that the maintenance of viable rural communities in Scotland should be based on a healthy agriculture and other rural industries.

Forestry. The SLF recognises the fundamental role of forestry in the rural economy. Forestry has always been an integral part of the Scottish Countryside. The expansion of forestry is supported and the SLF will seek fiscal and economic moves that will stimulate the production of timber and a sustainable planting programme to provide a valuable resource in an environment, and landscape that is of benefit to the public.

Fish Farming. The SLF views fish farming from the point of view of a landowner rather than that of a producer. The Federation welcomes the contribution that fish farming is making to the rural economy and wishes to see its continued success. There is a continuing requirement to harmonize traditional land uses, conservation interests and the requirements of a new industry.

Sporting. Sporting activities are of enormous importance to the Scottish rural economy. They have a very significant economic role, particularly in remote areas. The SLF seeks to encourage both the conduct of sportings in an ethical and legal manner and the employment of adequate numbers of keepers who are essential to the proper running or sporting estates. The present system of Sporting Rates and the lack of harmonization between various parts of the United Kingdom is unfair to sporting interests in Scotland.

Pest Control. The Federation regularly reminds its members of the legal methods of control. In their own interests members are advised to place a clause in the contracts of their gamekeepers, enjoining them to use only legal methods of control. At the same time we seek public recognition and acceptance of the need for pest control in the interests of sporting, agriculture and conservation.

Environment & Amenity. The SLF fully supports measures to improve the Environment, to create better amenities for the public and to care for wildlife and the landscape. Landowners must manage their business taking account of these requirements, but they should not be expected to pay out of private funds for measures designed for public benefit alone.

Public Use of the Land. The SLF encourages responsible public access to the land. This is best achieved by education and by making information available so that public recreation can be integrated successfully into the activities and requirements of those who own and work the land. We believe that the problems of public access must be solved by consensus and not by confrontation.

Rural Housing. The Federation believes that landowners have a valuable role in the provision of housing for local people in rural areas. We shall be seeking to evaluate and explain this role to Scottish Homes and local authorities.

Taxation. By annual representations to the Chancellor of the Exchequer and by other means the Federation argues the case for a sensible tax regime for landowners. The SLF believes that Landowners should be treated for tax purposes as a business.

AIMS OF THE SLF

The aims of the SLF are to:

- Represent members at all Government levels.
- Help members solve problems connected with land ownership and use.
- Encourage beneficial legislation in the development of rural land.
- Brief MPs and Euro MPs, thus providing a strong Parliamentary and EEC lobby.
- Monitor all taxation matters affecting land.
- Provide an interchange of ideas on land ownership including an annual conference.
- Promote recognition of the responsibilities of owning land.
- Organise events, including the Game Fair, which promote the concept of mixed land use. (Members receive free entry to each of the three days of the Game Fair.)

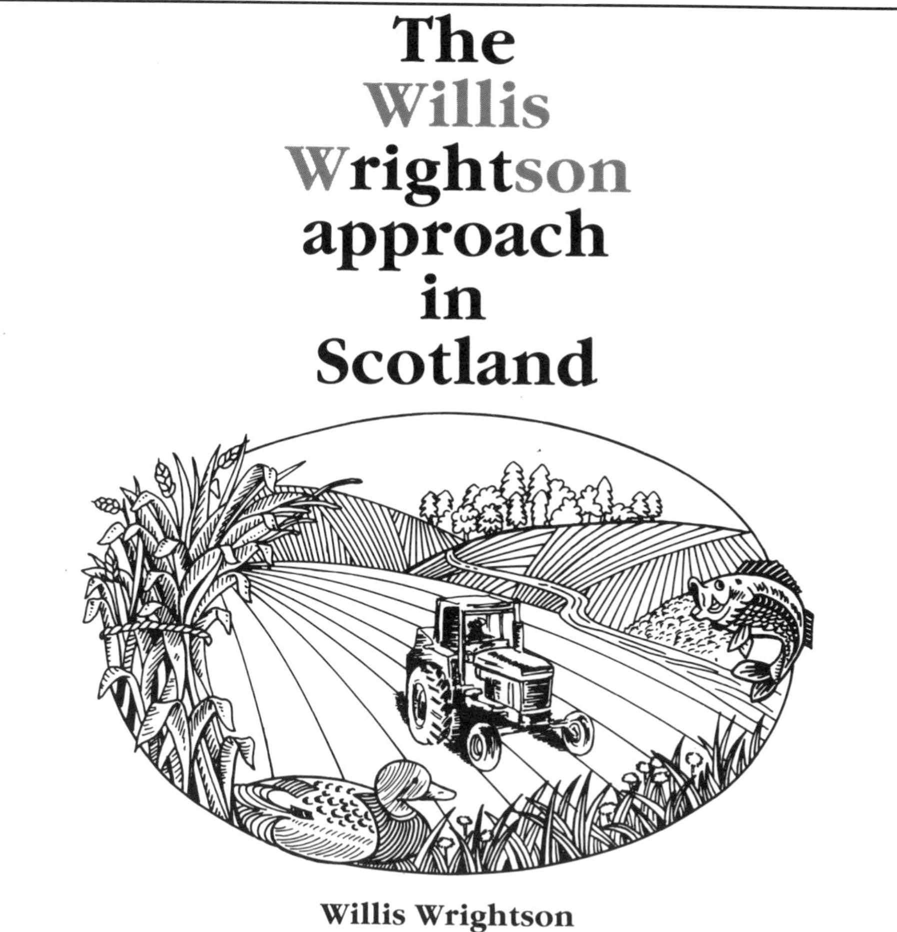
The
Willis
Wrightson
approach
in
Scotland

—Communicate the work and experience of SLF committees through the journal 'Landowning in Scotland' and through meetings.

Rural land ownership and the traditional rural industries of agriculture and forestry are entering a new era, one which will present new problems and new challenges. The Scottish Landowners' Federation is at the forefront helping landowners to cope with the changes which lie ahead.

SCOTTISH LANDOWNERS' FEDERATION

25 Maritime Street, Edinburgh, EH6 5PW.
Tel. 031-555-1031
Fax. 031-555-1052

OFFICE BEARERS

President
His Grace the Duke of Atholl.

Vice-Presidents
Major The Hon. Colin Dalrymple.
Colonel A. B. Houstoun.
P.C. Macdonald.
A.R. Trotter.

Convener
Patrick Gordon-Duff-Pennington.

Vice-Convener
Disney Barlow.

HQ STAFF

Director
Simon C. Fraser.
Legal Adviser
Paul Blacklock.

Administrative Secretary
Sheila M. M. Smail.

Editor/Advertising Manager
Mrs Doreen Graham.

REGIONAL STAFF

CENTRAL REGION

Regional Chairman
Major Brian H. Poett, Aberdona House, Alloa, Clackmannanshire, FK10 3QP.
Tel. 0259-50239

Regional Secretary
Iain Fraser, Dromana, 21 Edenbank Road, Cupar, Fife, KY15 4HE.
Tel. 0334-52869

Field Officer
A.A. (Sandy) Ogilvie, Drumshade Farm, Forfar, Angus, DD8 1QS.
Tel. 0575-72960

HIGHLAND REGION

Regional Chairman
John Mackenzie, Conan House, Conon Bridge, Ross-shire, IV7 8AL.
Tel. 0349-61101

Regional Secretary
Mrs Sally Braynion, Daigrambich Cottage, Croy, Inverness Inverness-shire, IV1 2PR.
Tel. 06678-373

Field Officers
Charles Hunter, Shore House, Lerags, Oban, Argyll, PA34 4SE.
Tel. 0631-64876
John Birnie, Druimchoille, Lennox Crescent, Fochabers, Morayshire, IV32 7ES.
Tel. (0343) 820040

NORTH EAST REGION

Regional Chairman
Andrew Dingwall-Fordyce, Brucklay Estate Office, Shevado, Maud, Peterhead, Aberdeenshire, AB4 8QN.
Tel. 07714-263

Regional Secretary
Captain Colin A. Farquharson, Estate Office, Mains of Haddo, Haddo House, Aberdeenshire, AB41 0ER.
Tel. 06515-664

Branch Secretary
K. Moubray Burnett, The Kennels, Straloch, Newmachar, Aberdeenshire, AB1 7UN.
Tel. 056182-256
Field Officer
Dr Gordon C. Sayer, 11 Wilson Road, Banchory, Kincardineshire, AB3 3UY.
Tel. 03302-4673

SOUTH EAST REGION

Regional Chairman
Michael Strang-Steel, Ravensheugh, Selkirk, TD7 5LS.
Tel. 0750-21766
Regional Secretary
Mrs Anne Fleming, Beechwood, Whitemire, Duns, Berwickshire, TD11 3PY.
Tel. 089-081-521.

Field Officer
Don Macfariane, Shepherds Cottage, Mossburnford, Jedburgh, Roxburghshire, TD9 6QS.
Tel. 08354-264

SOUTH WEST REGION

Regional Chairman
J. William Clark-Maxwell, Speddoch, Dumfries, DG2 9UB.
Tel. 038782-342

Regional Secretary
W. Richard Ellis, 13 Ridgepark Drive, Lanark, ML11 7PG.
Tel. 0555-4179

Branch Secretaries
Mrs. P. K. Anderson, Orchard Farm, Kirkmichael, Ayrshire, KA19 7JY.
Tel. 06555-209
Mrs Maureen McFarlane, 17 Strathearn Road, Clarkston, Glasgow, G76 7TY.
Tel. 041-664-1831

Branch Sec./Field Officer
Mrs Esme Forbes, Newpark, Brydekirk, Annan, Dumfriesshire, DG12 5LP.
Tel. 0576-3221

Field Officer
James Campbell, 9 Allenfield Road, Ayr, KA7 3JN.
Tel. 0292-265030

BELL-INGRAM
FORESTRY
&
BARCLAYS
SCOTLAND
Together provide the complete forestry package
COMPREHENSIVE WOODLAND, FORESTRY AND RURAL MANAGEMENT.
FULL ADMINISTRATION OF ALL GRANT SCHEMES, ENVIRONMENTAL ASSESSMENTS AND LANDSCAPE DESIGNS.
EXPERT TIMBER SALES ADVICE FROM VOLUME ESTIMATION TO MARKETING AND CONTRACT MANAGEMENT.
FLEXIBLE FINANCE STRUCTURED TO MEET ALL YOUR INDIVIDUAL REQUIREMENTS.
for full details contact;
BELL-INGRAM Forestry,
Durn, Isla Road, Perth PH2 7HF
Telephone 0738 21121

WILLIS WRIGHTSON

Willis Wrightson Scotland Ltd. is part of the Willis Faber Group, one of the world's largest insurance brokers with an enviable reputation for quality, integrity and service.

For many years we have been proud to be associated with the Scottish Landowners Federation as their official insurance advisers. This association has given us the understanding and experience to develop special insurance arrangements for Farmers and Estate Owners.

Our Agricultural Division will discuss with you the assets and liabilities of your enterprise and design an individual programme to protect these. Buildings, Farm Property and Liabilities can all be covered in a single policy to keep your administration to a minimum. Our market knowledge enables us to keep your protection costs very competitive and a discount is available for Federation members.

We are also market leaders in the insurance of Growing Timber. Despite the disastrous storms in recent years, cover is still available for windblow as well as fire and extends to include fire fighting and site clearance costs.

Willis Consulting Ltd., also part of the Willis Faber Group, are one of the largest firms of independent financial advisers in the U.K. Members of IMRO, the Investment Management Regulatory Organisation, we offer a comprehensive range of financial advice to individuals, partnerships and companies either directly or through professional advisers such as stockbrokers, chartered accountants or solicitors.

Our well established, financially secure base enables Willis Consulting to offer security, quality and continuity of service. Our clients can be assured that their affairs are being handled by a major independent firm with a first class reputation for professionalism and excellence. Above all they are founded on personal service based on the knowledge of particular circumstances, individual recommendations and continuous reviews as our clients circumstances and needs change.

The service which is confidential includes inheritance tax mitigation, pensions planning, life insurance protection, capital investment, funding for school fees, private medical and permanent health insurance, regular monthly savings and personal equity plans, mortgage and financial planning.

Our business has been built on many years of high quality service to clients. If you are seeking advice which is individual, informed and impartial, contact any of our four offices in Scotland.

REDUNDANT ASSETS ON THE FARM - OPTIONS FOR DEVELOPMENT

by Angus Cheape

During recent years, pressure has grown on farmers and estate owners to maximise income from areas other than their immediate farming enterprises, all of which have suffered considerable reductions in profitability across the board.

"Diversification with the farming enterprise has become a phrase which farmers are either wary of, or ignore, as they have seen so many promising entrepreneurial ideas leave larger holes in pockets than less ambitious projects based to a greater extent on traditional enterprises.

One area where there is definite scope for either maximising income, or releasing capital funds, is in the identification of under-used assets on the farm and estate. Following the widespread amalgamation of farms in the 1960s and 1970s these assets primarily come in the form of cottages no longer required because of labour reductions, and traditional farmbuildings which have become outdated by advances in modern day agriculture and progressive mechanisation.

Where political pressure has forced landowners into considering these alternatives, it comes as a pleasant surprise to many that the government have seen fit to relax planning controls over the past two years to encourage this form of diversification. There are also generous grants available from various bodies to lessen the conversion costs.

All factors, however, must be considered carefully before undertaking such development. Most importantly, are the buildings far enough from the centre of operations so that their disposal will not affect the integrity of the remainder of the property? Secondly, are the buildings well situated within a population catchment area, or within an area of high amenity? Lastly, the relative merits of an owner undertaking a project himself, or selling out to an independent developer, must be carefully balanced. Inevitably the prevailing cost of borrowing will tend to determine the ultimate feasibility of any individual development.

Financial assistance is available through the Department of Agriculture Farm Diversification Grant Scheme, and the Scottish Development Agency Better Business Services Scheme, both of which will meet up to 50% of the costs of a feasibility study.

Opportunities to sell bare land for development rely to a large extent on land use zoning as recommended by local planning authorities. Many variable factors are taken into account, and it is possible for potential sellers to consult very closely with planning officials before Local Plans are published in their final form.

Langley-Taylor are in direct contact with the Centre of Rural Buildings in Aberdeen. During the course of the next few years it is hoped that there will be more integration of the expertise that can be provided by an established firm of land agents with the more specialist inputs of the Centre of Rural Buildings. It is of enormous importance that "windfall capital" is secured for farmers and landowners, but long-term interests can only be protected if the advice available is both comprehensive and fully informed.

Angus Cheape is a partner in Langley-Taylor of Edinburgh and London.

Langley-Taylor

10 Great Stuart Street
EDINBURGH EH3 7TN

32 St James Street
LONDON SW1A 1HT

UNIQUE DAILY NEWSPAPER

The 'Press & Journal', one of Scotland's leading daily newspapers is probably unique in that it is the most farming orientated in the United Kingdom, being pre-eminent in its coverage of the farming scene in the North and North-east of Scotland. The award twinning agricultural team, farming editor Bill Howatson and farming correspondent Liz Fowler, bring you all the latest developments locally nationally and internationally.

In addition to daily agricultural coverage of the news, the latest market prices and industry intelligence, there is an in-depth round-up of features, analysis, profiles, and opinion in the weekly tabloid Farm Journals an eight page pull-out with the 'Press & Journal' every Saturday. The newspaper makes a significant contribution within the Farming Industry in Scotland.

CO-OPERATION IN THE 1990S

By Edward Rainy Brown,
Chief Executive, Scottish Agricultural Organisation Society Limited.

A resurgence of interest in co-operation in the 1990s, almost one hundred years after farmers first adopted the principle, seems likely,. Changes in the market place, as the industry comes to terms with GATT, reducing EC support and a totally different agribusiness structure surrounding the farm enterprise, underline the weakness of the individual farmer buyer or seller.

Co-operation in Scotland will never be the same as it is in some other European countries, but we start the decade with, by UK standards, a relatively bold co-operative sector, and a positive attitude to the need for farmers to relate together to the opportunities which exist to improve their own business viability, through involvement beyond the farm gate.

Scotland has not, as yet, entered into the correct round of rationalisation between co-operatives. The existence of the Federal United Farmers Ltd, on the supply side, has undoubtedly been a factor sustaining the smaller co-operatives concerned. There is also evidence that steps to improve the management of many co-operatives have been successful and, despite diminishing markets, their financial performances have been better than in preceding years.

The increasingly difficult economic environment in which farmers are operating has produced a renewal of interest in the use of co-operation to strengthen the position of the individual producer. The concentration of national and multi-national supply businesses, and the reducing number of major buyers of produce, has to be added Scotland's distance from the centre of the European market. Producers are acknowledging the need for change and the fact that only by operating together can the address many of the commercial opportunities which remain.

Co-operative marketing developments are being pro- gressed at a faster rate than has been experienced for many years. The sectors involved include lamb (largely in anticipation of the termination of the sheepmeat regime), beef, soft fruit, and vegetables. Scottish consumers, even more enthusiastically than those in the rest of the UK, have taken to the concept of supermarket purchasing, and this and the rapid development of new stores in Scotland have produced a demand for locally-sourced fresh produce that has particularly assisted Scottish fruit and vegetable production.

Farmers are also exploring new types of enterprise, for a number of which the co-operative model has ben adopted. These include cashmere fibre production and marketing and organic produce marketing.

The most dramatic new co-operative development in recent years has been the establishment of a nationwide network of machinery rings. This is a form of co-operative, the principles of which have been imported from West Germany. The basic purpose of these groupings is to rationalise the use of farm machinery and labour. With markets from which it is more and more difficult to increase returns, attention has switched to the cost side of the business, and the machinery ring is a mechanism by which, through a co-ordinated approach, the overall machinery cost base can be reduced,. Some farmers may dispense with machinery, calling upon others through the rings to provide them with the services they require, whilst other businesses may actually expand their machinery utilisation by selling interest in this type of co-operative in Scotland, and six machinery rings have been established.

The operation of a machinery ring is facilitated by modern information technology centering on a database of information about members' requirements and capabilities. It is expected that other services may develop from the base in due course. That has been the experience in Germany and Austria.

Several factors combine in Scotland to give a positive outlook for agricultural co-operation. Many of the established co-operatives are performing well above their industry averages in increasingly difficult markets. Farmers themselves are demonstrating an acceptance of the need for change and the role of co-operatives, both new and established, is acknowledged more widely than it has been for some time. The prospect for positive development of co-operation in the 1990's is good. It will be essential to secure the position of farming in a more complex and more difficult economic and political environment.

RURAL INDUSTRY TRAINING

1991 heralds a significant change to the provision of training in rural Scotland.

ATB Scotland has been developing a Training Service over the last 24 years and is now directed and managed in Scotland for Scotland.

The ability to deliver training to the most remote communities or the largest of companies gives an indication of the scale of operation and attention to detail.

Almost any training requirement can be met by over 650 trained Instructors or Tutors.

Instructors and Tutors are people who regularly practice their skills and are drawn from all sectors of Business and Industry. The Training of Trainers courses carefully develop the individual Instructor/Tutors abilities to communicate effectively. Such training is available to individuals or as a package for the larger businesses.

Practical craft skills can be taught to the novice or those who want to keep up to date.

The need for sound management skills is highlighted by Technical and Financial Business Management Training. Employment Law and the skills needed to manage people also feature in the skills to be taught.

ATB Scotland training methods focus directly on the needs of the individual. Great emphasis is placed on participation during training with each trainee able to do the job at the end of the training.

Keeping abreast of changes in Legislation is important to the progressive business and new courses are being developed to meet this need. As a leading Training Body in the Rural sector the need to establish acceptable standards is very important. An ATB Scotland Certificate means Quality Training.

Whether your requirement is for traditional skills or new activities or enterprises, good training at a reasonable cost is available.

Should you be unsure of your training requirements contact your ATB Scotland Adviser and discuss the situation. This initial Advisory service is free.

Benefit now from your truly Local Training Service. Contact your local Training Adviser (listed in the telephone book under ATB Scotland or ring 0738 31481).

THE AGA COOKER – IDEAL FOR COUNTRY LIVING

Conjuring up culinary delights, providing warmth to the kitchen and always ready when you need it; the AGA epitomises good living and good taste and is equally at home in the town or in the country.

The Aga operates on the heat storage principle. It has a relatively small energy source (gas, oil, solid fuel or off-peak electricity) and the heat from this source is stored by the iron castings inside the cooker. To retain this stored heat, the AGA is highly insulated and, to ensure that the pre-determined temperatures are maintained for the cast-iron hotplates and ovens, the cooker has automatic thermostatic control.

The Aga cooker is available in both two an four oven versions and the AGA reputation for cooking excellence lies with its cast iron ovens. An all round heat radiates onto the food from the castings, and because there is no direct flame or element within the oven, every cubic inch of the oven can be utilised and the food does not dry out.

The two oven AGA, is the more popular model. The top oven is a Roasting/Baking Oven with a Simmering Oven below, both are able to take a 28lb/13kg turkey. Both ovens are also ventilated into the flue, so the bonus is that even when baking kippers or poaching sole, the oven cooking smells are taken away to the outside.

Aga cookers are available in a choice of seven colours: red, blue, green, brown, cream, black or white. There is a choice of fuel too: propane gas (Calor), natural gas, oil, solid fuel or electricity, - using the off-peak Economy 7 tariff. Most models can provide a hot water facility of 90 gals/410 litres over 24 hours, whereas central heating can be provided by a matching Agamatic boiler fitted next to the cooker.

For further information contact: Robert Hope 0738 26931

THE SCOTTISH VETERINARY INVESTIGATION SERVICE

Dr Karl A. Linklater

The Scottish Veterinary Investigation Service is an integral part of The Scottish Agricultural College. Its prime objective is to provide a comprehensive range of services to protect the health of farm animals in Scotland. To achieve this it operates a network of eight Veterinary Investigation Centres which are spread throughout the country. These are based at Aberdeen, Ayr, Dumfries, Edinburgh, Inverness, Perth, St. Boswells and Thurso. Each Centre is managed by a Senior Veterinary Investigation officer who is supported by other veterinary staff, scientific officers, clerical and other lay staff.

The major function of the SVIS is to provide a diagnostic service for veterinary surgeons in practice to aid them in the diagnosis and investigation of diseases or on regular health and production monitoring programmes for farm animals in Scotland. The services provided include pathology (ie post mortem examination of carcases), microbiology (ie a range of tests covering most common bacteria, viruses and mycoplasmas), biochemistry, parasitology, serology and haematology. All these laboratory methods are monitored through internal quality control and external quality assessment ensuring that the results provided are accurate and reproducible.

The SVIS works closely with other services of The Scottish Agricultural College, the Veterinary Investigation Service of MAFF, the MAFF Lasswade Unit, the Central Veterinary Laboratory, Weybridge and the Animal Diseases Research Association's Moredun Research Institute. All of these provide laboratory support and scientific backup to the SVIS to form an extremely strong and unique service in the diagnosis, control and research of animal diseases.

By the nature of this work the SVIS provides a link between the farm and animal disease research. it maintains close links with the veterinary schools in Scotland, and the relevant agricultural research institutes, especially the Moredun Research Institute which supplies specialist diagnostic support and scientific advice in biochemistry, pathology and microbiology. At its most rudimentary level, research and development (R & D) involves the ad hoc investigations of unusual disease outbreaks. Through this work the SVIS has, over the years, played a key role in the identification of many new disease entities, eg infectious abortion of ewes, cerebrocortical necrosis in sheep, infectious bovine rhinotracheitis, jaagziekte of sheep, bovine virus diarrhoea and many others. Many of these have gone on to become important areas of research at the Moredun and other research institutes leading to the development of new vaccines and other measures for the control of animal diseases in the field. The SVIS also plays an important role in evaluating the practical value of new products through field trials on commercial farms.

Another important function of the SVIS is to supply laboratory support for the Animal Health Division of the Department of Agriculture for Scotland in connection with the statutory control of diseases such as brucellosis, tuberculosis, and salmonellosis. All eight laboratories are actively involved in the monitoring of poultry flocks for the presence of salmonellosis and each has also been heavily involved in the diagnosis of bovine spongiform encephalopathy (BSE) throughout the country, playing a major part in the disposal of the carcases of affected animals. The Service is also heavily involved in the control of diseases which are communicable to man and liaises regularly with local medical and environmental health authorities.

By the nature of their work and through their close contact with field problems presented by veterinary surgeons in practice, Veterinary Investigation Officers build up a unique knowledge of diseases occurring in their area. In addition, through contacts with professional colleagues throughout Britain and further afield, they have access to information on national and international trends in animal diseases, on the occurrence of any new disease syndrome plus the latest information on new diagnostic methods and control measures. This proved invaluable in the recent crisis brought about by the appearance of BSE in Scotland.

The SVIS is therefore the only organisation regularly collecting reliable information on the pattern of animal diseases throughout Scotland. The collation of this information, along with that of colleagues in England and Wales, provides the basis for national disease surveillance.

As well as staff which are actively involved in the provision of a diagnostic and advisory service, there are other specialist Senior Veterinary Investigation Officers who are available to provide advice on the diseases and husbandry of a range of farm stock. These cover cattle health and production, pig health, poultry health and production, sheep diseases and farmed fish. Some specialised services provided by the SVIS include the following:

Game Bird Diagnostic Services

Problems of health and productivity are becoming of major importance in artificially reared gamebirds such as pheasants and partridges and parasitic burdens in red grouse can dramatically reduce the profitability of grouse moors. By their strategic location, the eight Centres of the SVIS are able to provide a wide range of laboratory services for game bird keepers throughout Scotland. Veterinary Investigation officers will give advice on the diagnosis, treatment and control of game birds and are happy to undertake on site consultations which are backed up by a veterinary surgeon who specialises in the problems of game birds and by colleagues in the Poultry Department of SAC.

Equine Diagnostic Services

An extensive range of laboratory tests is available to aid the maintenance of health in horses at all of the Centres. These include selective and comprehensive haematological assessments, biochemical investigations of metabolic dysfunction, microbiological examinations including serological and cultural evidence of viral infections and, of course, routine parasitological tests. The St. Boswells VI Centre is approved for monitoring horses for contagious equine metritis.

Fish Diagnostic Services

A veterinary surgeon specialising in fish problems is located at the Inverness VI Centre and is available to

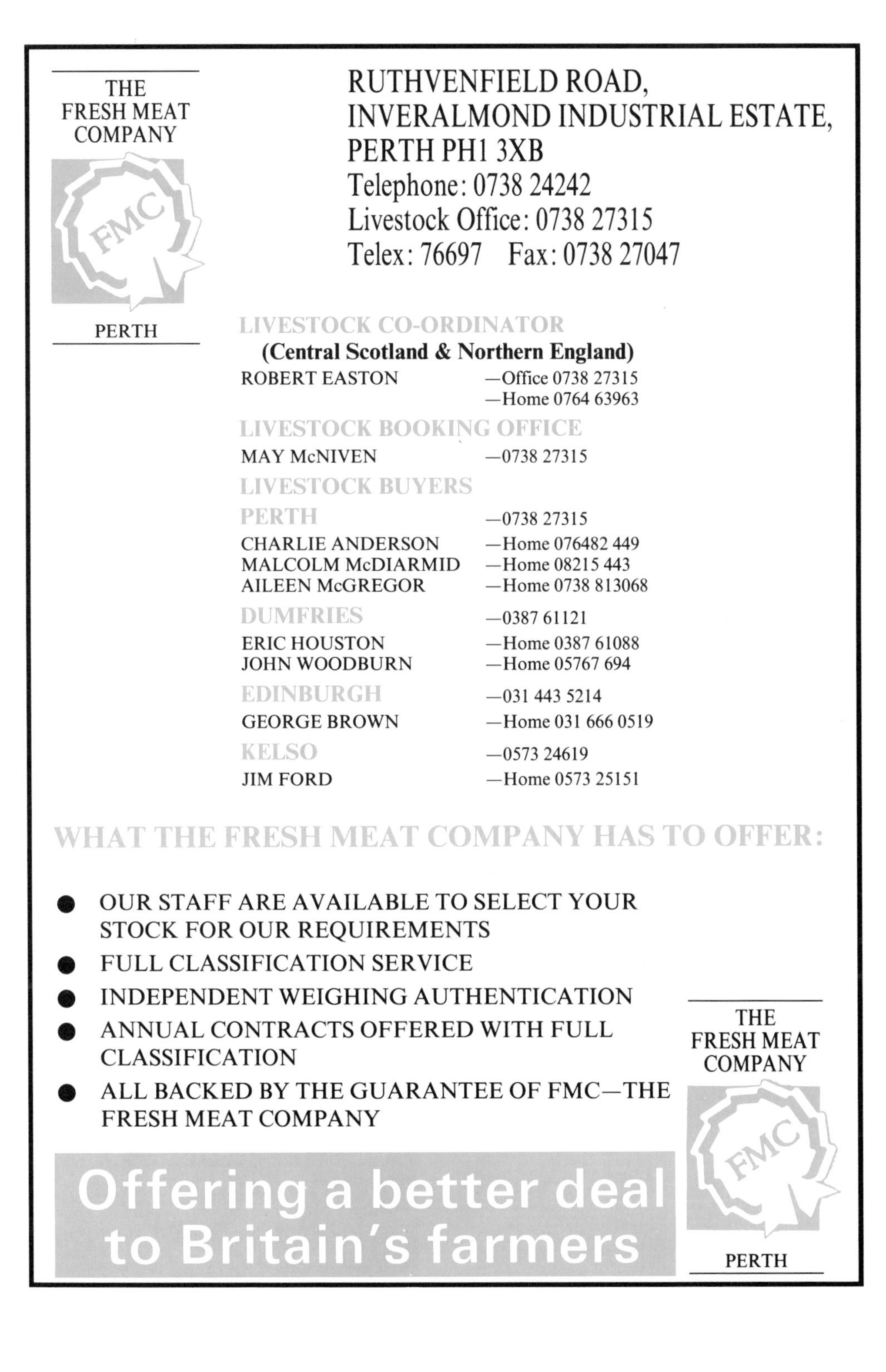
THE
FRESH MEAT
COMPANY
FMC
PERTH
RUTHVENFIELD ROAD,
INVERALMOND INDUSTRIAL ESTATE,
PERTH PH1 3XB
Telephone: 0738 24242
Livestock Office: 0738 27315
Telex: 76697 Fax: 0738 27047
LIVESTOCK CO-ORDINATOR
(Central Scotland & Northern England)
ROBERT EASTON —Office 0738 27315
—Home 0764 63963
LIVESTOCK BOOKING OFFICE
MAY McNIVEN —0738 27315
LIVESTOCK BUYERS
PERTH —0738 27315
CHARLIE ANDERSON —Home 076482 449
MALCOLM McDIARMID —Home 08215 443
AILEEN McGREGOR —Home 0738 813068
DUMFRIES —0387 61121
ERIC HOUSTON —Home 0387 61088
JOHN WOODBURN —Home 05767 694
EDINBURGH —031 443 5214
GEORGE BROWN —Home 031 666 0519
KELSO —0573 24619
JIM FORD —Home 0573 25151
WHAT THE FRESH MEAT COMPANY HAS TO OFFER:
OUR STAFF ARE AVAILABLE TO SELECT YOUR STOCK FOR OUR REQUIREMENTS
FULL CLASSIFICATION SERVICE
INDEPENDENT WEIGHING AUTHENTICATION
ANNUAL CONTRACTS OFFERED WITH FULL CLASSIFICATION
ALL BACKED BY THE GUARANTEE OF FMC—THE FRESH MEAT COMPANY
Offering a better deal
to Britain's farmers
THE
FRESH MEAT
COMPANY
FMC
PERTH

provide a veterinary consultative service to the industry throughout Scotland covering all aspects of management. Apart from laboratory diagnosis of fish diseases, routine health monitoring and on site consultancy services are available. The service is available for cultured, wild or ornamental fish.

Advanced Breeding Services

In 1987 an additional Centre was set up to deal with the demand for modern technology in the field of animal breeding. A complete range of breeding services to cattle, sheep and goat farmers is offered, pioneered within the Scottish agricultural research service over the last five years. Services available include semen handling and storage, artificial insemination of sheep and goats, embryo transfer in sheep, goats and cattle, and freezing and storage of embryos.

Premium Health Scheme for Sheep

The SVIS offers a health accreditation scheme for sheep in the form of the Premium Health Scheme for Sheep (PHSS).

This is offered to producers and sellers of female breeding sheep in Scotland through their veterinary practices. Flocks registered under the PHSS are monitored for freedom from enzootic abortion and membership will be of greatest benefit to those flocks producing cast ewes for further breeding or selling breeding ewe lambs. Monitoring involves the examination of all aborted foetuses and placentas and serological examination of a selection of the flock. The investigations are detailed and thorough and provide a full differential diagnosis of the cause of abortion, not simply EAE. In the Highlands and Islands Development Board area the scheme is operated by the Highlands and Islands Sheep Health Association with the same rules.

The Scottish Veterinary Investigation Service therefore now offers a comprehensive service in animal health and production to livestock owners in Scotland operating in conjunction with veterinary surgeons in private practice to provide a "unique partnership in animal health".

Dr. Karl A. Linklater, Director of the SAC Veterinary Investigation Service

THE SCOTCH WHISKY INDUSTRY AND FARMING

These two traditional industries have been part of the fabric of Scottish life for centuries. They are very closely related, but the links may seem a little tenuous nowadays.

In the beginning, it could be argued that distilling was an early diversification for farmers and crofters (with better future prospects than modern set-aside, that's for sure!!). To begin with, distilling was a seasonal occupation, the year starting as soon as new crop barley would break dormancy. Coincidentally, it was subsequently shown that the best quality spirit was made during the cool weather period from November to April. Seasonal labour was therefore available to move from the land into the distillery. In due time, as distilleries became larger and more prosperous, they tended to run their own farms (and some still do).

On the island of Islay, as well as returning to the land in spring, man would take to the moors to cut peats for fuel and for flavouring the malt in the distillery kilns. This process continues as it has through the centuries. Interestingly enough, at Bowmore Distillery, where the malt is still produced in the old-fashioned way, there is a lovely conservation story to tell. The malt is now dried using hot air from a waste heat recovery system, but peat is still burned to flavour it, as practised.for over 200 years. Since the coming of the maltster, regrettably, the farmer and distiller are not now so close. Gone are the days when the barley grower would pop in to see his product being malted, mashed, fermented and distilled. Customer/contractor relationships were kept healthy and often enhanced over a dram! A very worthwhile exercise and thankfully, once again primary food producers are beginning to waken up to the idea that the end point is not the crop going out from the farm gate!

THE NATURAL CYCLE

Right from the early days when those working the land would use surplus grain to distil their own 'water of life', agriculture and distilling have been complementary industries.

Times have changed of course but the two are still part of a highly efficient natural cycle. The finest cereals are used in the production of Scotch whisky distillers are looking for grain of a specific quality which will give the maximum spirit yield. They therefore provide a market for top quality malting barley, together with wheat or maize for grain distilling.

Scottish farmers have recently provided some of the best samples of malting barley in the British Isles and the evolution of varieties that will perform well in Scottish conditions should enable growers to benefit from the premiums paid for the right quality: especially as there is an increasing requirement for the crop with the distilling industry in Scotland presently in a period of growth.

In theory, spirit can be made from any cereal. Nowadays, the proprietary whisky brands contain mainly grain spirit together with a secret proportion of several different malt whiskies which gives the blend its individual character.

Malt whisky can however be made only from malted barley and is usually marketed as the product of a single 'named' distillery. But this is only part of the story . . .

In order to produce spirit and ultimately whisky; the distiller needs fermentable sugars and these are available from the starch content of the cereal which the farmer provides.

After this prime raw material has been extracted, what remains is an excellent source of energy, protein, oil, minerals and fibre which the distiller, in his role of supplier, can then offer back to the farmer as animal feeds.

The largest supplier of these distillery feeds is Borthwick and Glasgow based subsidiary of United Distillers which has been funding research into the nutritional and economic benefits of incorporating products such as Draff and Distillers Dark Grains in diets for dairy cows, beef cattle and sheep.
As more spirit is being distilled, there is now an increased supply of such feeds and many new uses for them have been discovered. Great attention is paid to processing and quality control to ensure that these products are of a good, wholesome and consistent composition.

There is also the assurance that as long as there are distilleries throughout Scotland using the best raw materials to produce the finest whisky then there will also be a source of natural feedstuffs for the livestock farmer.

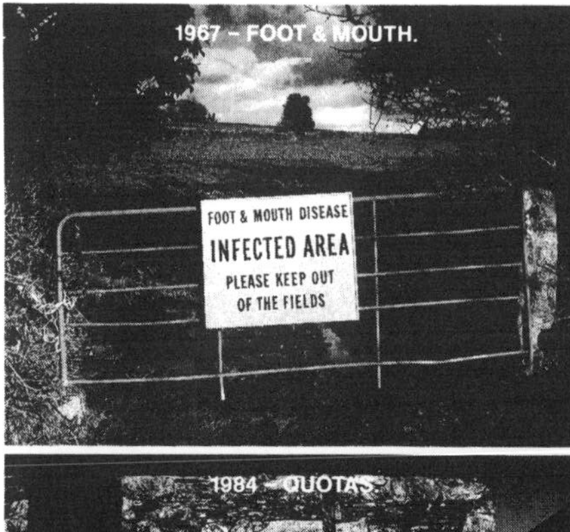

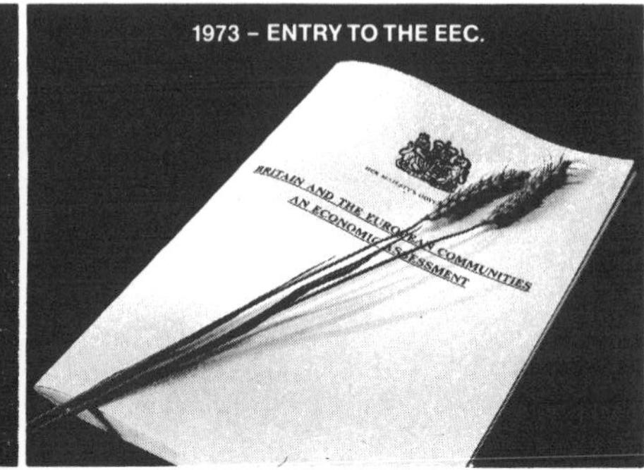

1984 – QUOTAS.

1992?

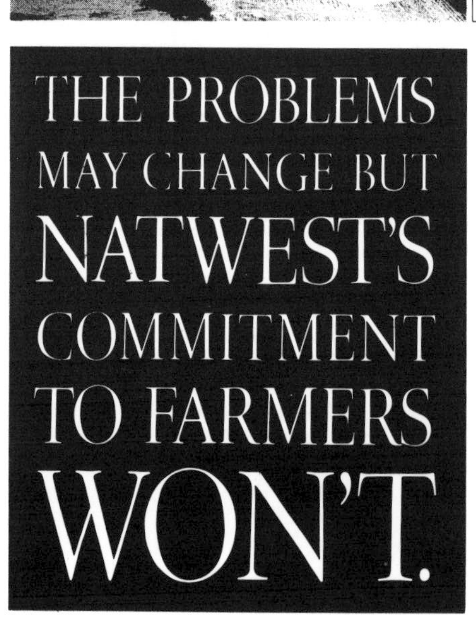

Over the past few years fundamental changes have taken place in agriculture.

And, with 1992 only a few years away, the changes are likely to continue.

This may mean that you, as a farmer, will continue to need some support.

Perhaps you feel you need financial help on how to improve your business?

Or financial guidance about the future?

Perhaps you need finance for expanding your farm, or to buy new equipment and machinery to make it more successful?

Whatever your particular situation, you will find NatWest has a wealth of experience in farming. Come and see us.

With our help, the continuous changes that face farmers could lead to profit, not problems.

FORESTRY

QUALITY COUNTS

by Fraser Barraclough FRICS,
Director, Bell-Ingram, Perth

For a variety of widely differing reasons much of Britain's forestry, both large and small scale, has either started off from day one as a poor quality exercise or has suffered from lack of management and attention as the years have gone by.

Not all woods are established with the prime aim of producing timber. Many woods established in an Estate context may well have another primary purpose eg to improve sporting potential, to provide shelter for livestock or perhaps just to improve the general amenity and environment of the Estate. In these situations, particularly through the years when income from early thinnings was minimal, or even negative, there was often little incentive to the owner of the woodland to manage his woodland in accordance with good silvicultural practice. As a consequence, there are many woodlands on Estates which have been under-thinned and which will never produce the volume or quantity of timber they were capable of doing. In other cases, whereas the original owner of the property may have had a keen interest in woodland, a subsequent owner or a subsequent generation may lack that interest and again, as a result, attention and management during the early production years has often been missing and the whole long term benefit of the wood substantially depreciated.

Perhaps in more recent years however the biggest culprit in almost encouraging poor quality forestry has been the recent Schedule D tax incentive support system. The tax incentive method of support did have considerable benefits for forestry and encouraged the flow of many thousands of pounds into the countryside, creating new woods and creating jobs. It has to be admitted however that one drawback of the system was that whereas full tax allowance was given on all normal costs of establishment, no tax allowance was given on the acquisition of land. Accordingly, the system positively encouraged the acquisition of cheap (and therefore poor) land even where the costs of establishing such land were relatively high. As a result of this policy many thousands of acres of young plantations have been established on exposed, hard, unproductive land on much of which it is difficult to believe a crop of commercial timber will ever mature even with the help of significant doses of phosphate and other fertilisers.

As in many aspects of life, quality in the establishment and management of a woodland is important.

Quality Land

The importance of quality starts with the land itself. On a poor site the costs of establishment are likely to be higher, physical growth is likely to be lower and the resultant crop is likely to be both later in arriving and poorer in quality. To the extent that the aim of a national forest policy is to produce volumes of timber to combat the import deficit situation, then it must be in the national interest to grow trees on land which produces as much timber as possible.

Physical growth is not only relevant to the import saving role. One of the increasingly important roles a forest has to play, particularly in the eyes of the public, is that of combating the greenhouse effect. In simple terms, the more vigorously a tree is growing the greater will be its ability to fix carbon and contribute to combating the greenhouse effect. On this very important environmental factor good quality growth resulting in a greater ability to contribute to the fixing of carbon out of the atmosphere.

Also of increasing and enduring importance is the factor of amenity. A woodland is an important feature of any scene and its design and location can either make or mar a rural landscape. Amenity is also often to a certain extent subjective, but many would take the view that the open expanses of the higher hills and moors have a certain grandeur which is all their own and which may not always be compatible with a commercial woodland operation. Many upland areas, inherently more sheltered and with a more fertile soil, may well lack such intrinsic visual interest and not only be capable of producing better quality timber but also have the potential for the creating of a much more interesting and amenable landscape than currently exists. Furthermore, good quality land in a more sheltered location tends to lead to longer crop rotations, thereby reducing the periods during which the perhaps unsightly phase of clear fell and replanting subsists.

Quality Establishment

Many jobs can only be done once and if they are not done properly at that time will effect the growth and quality of the plantation for the whole of its life. Good quality control right from the start is therefore essential if a woodland owner is to obtain the best potential from his site. There is no subsequent cure for the choice of poor quality plants; badly designed or implemented drainage schemes may be very difficult or costly to amend, with the possibility that they may never be as good as a drainage scheme properly thought out and properly established in the first place; and poor ploughing or other forms of ground preparation may well get the young trees off to a poor start from which they will always suffer. Good quality establishment is therefore of prime importance in achieving the optimum results from a woodland, and with only one beginning in every fifty or sixty years of the rotation life it is doubly important to ensure that that beginning is the best possible.

Quality Management

To a Forester or Land Agent the lack of management which sometimes occurs to plantations is almost a criminal offence. Having taken the care to choose the right ground and establish it well with the right plants, there is nothing to be gained and a lot to lose by not taking the little care needed to ensure that an established young plantation is able to continue to grow productively. The most essential features are vermin control, drain maintenance and ensuring that fire hazard is minimised.

As soon as the plantation reaches the stage where thinnings can be taken, proper management and marking of thinnings is essential both in terms of the cost of carrying out the work, the level of return obtained from it and, most importantly of all in the early stages, ensuring that the maximum benefit is gained by the trees remaining so that they are able to grow successfully onto the next production stage. Quality management also should infer that, during these years, the work carried out is that which is prudently required and that it is carried out at a minimum cost. Whereas it is a false economy not to carry out important items of care and attention during these periods of a plantation's life, it is certainly economically foolish to spend large amounts of money on work which is an unnecessary embellishment.

Quality Product

With the setting up of new thermo-chemical pulp mills in Britain, notably most recently at Irvine and at Shotton, the demand for younger thinnings has been underwritten, in a physical scene, and hopefully the days when early thinning was uneconomic and when such thinnings as were taken had to be exported, are now largely past. However, looking to the long term Britain's relative advantage, in a world scale, must be producing quality timber. In terms of Europe, Britain is certainly one of the more productive forestry growing areas. However, looking purely at the production of pulp there are many regions in the sub-tropical zones of the world where fast growing trees can be grown at rates which are staggering in UK or European terms and, particularly as these areas are developed more and more, it seems likely that they will achieve a considerable importance for the production of pure pulp material.

Britain's forests - particularly those on the better quality ground - do have the ability to produce good quality saw log material. In the long term the aim should be to make the most of this relative advantage and both plan to grow woods which have this potential and to manage them in the appropriate way. Whereas the existence of the large pulp processing industry within Britain will underwrite the income from early thinnings during the life of a woodland, the production of high quality sawmill timber should be the target which many woodland owners aim for.

C.O.S.H.H. REGULATIONS

by Jim Tassel

NEW HEALTH AND SAFETY REGULATIONS have come into force which will have a far reaching impact on estate and farm management.

They are the Control of Substances Hazardous to Health Regulations.

They are made under the Health and Safety at Work Act 1974 and are enforced by the Factory Agriculture and Quarries Inspectorate of the Health and Safety Executive.

Anyone who is an employer, manager or self employed needs to be aware of them and consider how they affect their business. They aim to control risks which vary widely from employer to employer. They do not follow a "rule book" approach but require every employer and self employed person to work out what their particular risks are and ways of protecting people against them. It is not only employees who are protected but anyone who may be put at risk such as neighbours and members of the public.

The consequences of ignoring or failing to comply with the Regulations are not only prosecution but also the disruption which a prohibition or improvement notice could cause. There are also major implications for claims by employees and others.

There is an increasing expectation that people's health at work will be safeguarded by an employer and a greater readiness to claim than in the past. Specific hazards such as noise have led to a spate of claims in recent years in some parts of industry, with a serious effect on employers liability insurance costs and this seems likely to spread into other health related claims.

Many people will have heard of COSHH. Some will have obtained a copy, but few have yet come to grips with its wide implications. It is a major overhaul of health related legislation and for the first time the best practice in this field has been translated into a set of legal requirements.

There are strong indications that many more people suffer ill health as a result of their work than suffer accidents. This ill health may build up over many years and is less obvious than an accident, but is no less capable of reducing or destroying their ability to work and support themselves.

The Regulations apply to a wide range of substances:

1. The majority of bought-in chemicals which are (or should be) labelled to show that they are hazardous and have the words toxic, very toxic, harmful, irritant or corrosive on the label, eg pesticides, building chemicals and some lubricants.

2. Substances generated during the work activity such as products, by-products or contaminants, eg dust from mouldy grain, engine exhaust fumes and dangerous gases in sumps and pits.

3. Micro-organisms which are work related (but not the annual flu virus) eg Weils disease and zoonoses.

4. Substantial quantities of any dust, even if it has little or no specific health risk.

5. A catch-all of anything similar to these.

Every employer or self employed person is required to conduct an assessment of the risk to health of every substance before it is taken into use for the first time. The assessment must particularly take note of any potential carcinogens (cancer causing agents) such as used engine oil or hardwood dust.

Before anyone gets to the stage of attempting assessments, there are two vital steps to be considered. The first is not a specific requirement of COSHH but is nevertheless important. It is simply management. Almost every employer has some part to play in successful implementation of COSHH and it is very helpful to work out an overall strategy of responsibilities first. There will also be significant numbers of records to keep and the best format for these needs careful thought.

The next step is to collect information.

What substances do you actually have to assess?

Make a list and if in doubt about a substance put it on. Then obtain as much information as you can about them from manufacturers safety data sheets, Health and Safety Executive publications and any other source of information which might be relevant.

Once you have collected this information you must put it together with a careful review of the way the substances are actually used to arrive at an assessment of the actual risks they present in practice.

From this the necessary precautions can be worked out.

Precautions are not just personal protection like gloves and respirators but include the search for safer substitutes and engineering controls such as exhaust ventilation and enclosure. In fact, personal protection is only a last resort if other methods fail although in many farm and estate activities it is the only realistic option.

After the precautions have been chosen comes the hardest but most important part of the process. This is implementation. The test of compliance with COSHH is not what is documented or the length of the assessment document but it is what happens in practice.

Are the people who use hazardous substances aware of the risks and the necessary precautions and do they take them? If not, all your assessment effort has been wasted.

The process does not stop there. The assessments have to be reviewed on an ongoing basis and a range of checks may have to be carried out such as atmospheric monitoring and checking of respiratory protection (except one shift disposable types) and local exhaust ventilation. All this has to be documented and records need to be kept for long periods (up to 30 years in the case of health and personal exposure records).

There will be cases where health records for health surveillance are called for. This does not necessarily mean full medical surveillance and could be very simple but prudent checks by managers, first aiders or other people with only a simple knowledge. We expect an increase in health related claims against employers liability insurance as the expectations of work people towards their health rise and as a spin-off of the "green" movement. (How many readers have consciously switched to lead free petrol or environment friendly washing powder as an example of increased awareness?).

The records required by COSHH are essential evidence to enable an employer or his insurers to establish at some future time, possibly half a lifetime away, that he made realistic assessments, took realistic precautions and provided appropriate training for all those at risk. It seems a heavy burden but will probably prove worthwhile in the long term.

There is a short term financial benefit however. COSHH focusses attention on the substances you use and many people have already been surprised at the large number that they buy and the duplications of suppliers and specifications. There are real savings to be made by rationalising. Also some substances unlikely ever to be used up are often found which it would be prudent to send for disposal.

The official guidance on COSHH suggests that most managers should be able to do the bulk of the risk assessment work themselves with perhaps an input from specialist help on particular topics such as atmospheric sampling but it does take time at the start.

The Regulations came into full effect on I January 1990 so it is important to give them careful attention straight away if you have not already done so.

As if COSHH were not enough, two other major Codes of Regulations are also coming along at the same time. The Noise at Work Regulations 1989 bring into force an EC directive from I January 1990 and the Electricity at Work Regulations 1989 come into force on I April 1990 and affect anyone involved in any way with the use of electricity at work, including the repair and maintenance of systems.

Free leaflets on all these topics can be obtained from the HSE offices in Edinburgh and Glasgow.

Taken together the next few months will need to be busy, ones indeed for estate and farm management if they are to come to grips with these Regulations.

J Tassel, MSc MIOSH RSP. Scottish Divisional Director of Hinton and Higgs (Consultants) Limited who are an associated Company of Willis Wrightson Scotland Limited and are Europes largest Safety Consultancy. Mr Tassel can be telephoned directly on 041-339 3573 or through his Head Office at the Firs, 20 Marcham Road, Abingdon, Oxon. OX14 1AA. Tel: 0235 24228.

ORGANIC FARMING - A FEASIBLE ALTERNATIVE?

Over the recent past, consumers have been persuaded to buy food which has been produced in a "more environmentally friendly" manner. Organic food is seen to fit their requirements and although still a small amount of total food production in the UK, it is expanding rapidly and likely to continue to do so for the foreseeable future. Demand outstrips supply with the shortfall being imported from principally Holland and West Germany. This is despite the fact that a large proportion of this produce could in practice be supplied by British Growers, given the recent incentives to adopt organic systems. Some organic movements have even called for government and public support to encourage "conversion of 20% of British farmland to organic production by the year 2000". (At present, there is perhaps 1-2% of farmland in organic production.)

But, lets put this into perspective. At the moment, demand for organic production is still relatively small. Volumes of sales of organic fruit and vegetables for instance, perhaps the most widely available types of organic food are, at present, at only around 1-5% of total fresh fruit and vegetable sales. Nevertheless, the organic market acts as a "niche market", a sort of "special brand name" product, which in practice, due to the surplus demand over supply, can obtain highly attractive premiums: Milling wheat for instance might obtain up to 100% premium, potatoes 25-50%, or even more. In an era with EEC surpluses, and output prices which reflect this, this could therefore be a market worth considering.

So, what is involved in practice, and could it be a feasible, more profitable alternative?

WHAT'S INVOLVED?

a. *Standards*

There are a number of different standards (do's and don'ts) established by a number of organic bodies over the years, to which organic farmers and growers may work to. Recently however, in order to try to co-ordinate all these standards, the Government has established UKROFS (United Kingdom Register of Organic Food Standards) as the national standards body. Individual organic bodies will need to register their standards with UKROFS and get them approved if they are to be acknowledged as producing bona-fide organic products. UKROFS is still in its infancy, but it will be the designated body responsible for certifying organic production under the EEC regulation now being drafted. There are no approved organic sector bodies as yet, but applications are being processed and it will not be long before the opportunity to join UKROFS approved organisations will be available. This article is therefore based on UKROFS standards. Adopting the approved organic practices should subsequently lead to farmers being awarded organic status - this in turn should allow the producer to market his product under an organic logo and hopefully obtain a premium.

Organic farming and the UKROFS standards aim to encourage:

(i) Well balanced, self contained farming systems - for example with arable by-products being used to feed livestock which in turn produce dung to fertilise crops.

(ii) Avoiding the use of non-permitted agrochemicals - eg. chemical sprays and fertilisers.

(iii) Animal health and welfare - this is of utmost importance in organic systems, and no activities must prejudice the welfare of the animal. Livestock management practice must be geared towards maintaining the animal in good health and as far as possible preventing conditions arising where conventional veterinary treatments become necessary. However conventional treatments may be used where it is necessary to save the animals life, prevent suffering, or to treat conditions where no preventative management is available. (The main exceptions are organophorphorus compounds, such as some wormers and sheep dips, which if used, will permanently exclude that animal from organic status. Often non-organophorphorus alternatives are available.)

b. *Converting to Organic*

Organic farming is not an easy option - it requires high levels of management and the adoption of husbandry practices which help avoid problems occurring as far as possible, or will reduce the occurrence of problems.

Conversion of the land to organic farming generally takes a minimum of 24 months from the last use of any prohibited treatment until the establishment of the first organic crop. Set-aside could be used to facilitate entry into an organic system.

There may in fact be a number of hill and upland farms who's grassland could meet these requirements already (lime and ground rock phosphates for instance are acceptable inputs) and they may be accepted by the certification authority without undergoing a further conversion period

Livestock must be produced organically in an organic system to satisfy most standards.

C. *Financial Effects*

Where a conversion phase is required, this can cause cashflow problems. Crop yields may fall by at least 20%, and output from say organic beef may be reduced by around 10-20%. Over this conversion period there will be little or no premium on produce. Whilst variable costs (sprays, fertilisers etc) would be expected to decrease, they may still be relatively high - alternative inputs may be available, but these can be costly (eg. organic feed for stock, organic fertilisers etc). There may be teething problems initially with this alternative approach to farming, which may mean that performance during this time does not achieve the longer term likely performance levels. Fixed costs on the farm may also be higher than when farming conventionally: more labour may be needed for instance (possibly more stock on the farm, more hand weeding etc) machinery costs may rise (more cultivation may be needed for weed control etc). Capital requirements and interest costs may also increase - particularly if stock needs to be bought. There may be other "hidden" costs to be carried too - for example, if over the winter to help maintain or improve fertility supply. Very careful financial feasibility assessment is required to examine whether the cashflow and profit implications of conversion and indeed, whether or not the farm is likely to be more profitable and viable in the long term once it becomes established as organic than it was before the change.

Certain farm types are likely to find it easier to convert than others - for instance farm systems with a higher proportion sensitive coastal areas and alpine regions and economy-based measures to implement environment policy.

The impact of environment-based measures over the next few years is therefore likely to be great and land users and land managers will have little choice but to come to terms with and accept such additional constraints on their freedom to use the land.

"Care for the environment" will be a war-cry heard for sometime to come and the present policy of the U.K. Government is likely to result in the introduction of other measures to achieve this end. We are told to expect a Government White Paper in the autumn of 1990 as an indicator of things to come. In addition the Council of Ministers of the EC has adopted the Regulation creating the European Environment Agency, an important step, again an indicator of the importance the EC attaches to the protection and proper management of the environment, a reflection locally of a view held worldwide. We are all bound to feel the influence of this need to conserve the environment, to a greater or lesser extent depending on where and how we live, and we ignore it at our peril.

ENVIRONMENTAL ISSUES IN THE COUNTRYSIDE

Professor David Atkinson. SAC ABERDEEN

The introduction of agriculture to a previously forested or natural environment represents the largest, single disturbance in terms of land use and environmental impact. All other changes, intensive compared to extensive farming systems, are relatively small compared to land being táken into agriculture. The change to agriculture results in a reduction in the numbers of noncrop plants, small animals and birds. Consideration of environmental matters in the countryside thus involves assessing the impact of land being in agriculture (or commercial forestry) at all and separately the environmental impact of the practices employed by farms and other rural businesses.

Rural Conservation

As agriculture (or commercial forestry) reduces the variety and extent of wildlife it follows that to maintain this major contribution to the amenity of the countryside, the amount of land used for agricultural production should be the minimum necessary. The logical consequences of this is that serious consideration must always bel given to maintaining those farm areas with poor production potential, eg corners adjacent to woodland, wet areas, stream banks etc as non-agricultural areas. Maximum conservation benefit from these areas will depend upon their being protected from agricultural inputs, especially fertilisers and pesticides. Conservation areas do require some positive management.

In addition to the maintenance of existing wildlife habitats, areas of non-agricultural land can be increased by taking land out of productive use. sat-aside, conservation headlands and farm ponds represent examples of this process. The current Government set-aside scheme was designed to take land out of production but stopped short of positively encouraging the use of such land for conservation although the self sown option within permanent fallow has some potential. As it is likely to take a significant length of time for arable weeds to decrease as the major component of the vegetation and for a wider range of species to develop, the current five year limit on the scheme is a major limitation. Leaving conservation headlands untreated with pesticide, allows the maintenance of the hedgerow flora and fauna. It also allows the use of the area as food and cover for game birds. The development of ponds in some wetland areas, of mixed species small woodland plantings, and tie return of "improved" grassland to heather moorland, all represent ways in which conservation potential and general amenity can be improved with little effect on total farm production or profitability. SAC Conservation Advisers can help with free general advice and with the preparation of farm conservation plans.

The Environmental Impact of Agricultural Production

Modern agricultural production influences the environment both in relation to the inputs it uses and as a consequence of the direct and indirect effects of husbandry and associated "value added" activities. The impact of nitrogenous fertilisers and pesticides has recently received much publicity. Pesticide residues in ground water and in food need to be minimised even though most modern pesticides are less harmful than many of the natural products contained in foods, eg aflotoxin in peanut butter. Contamination of the environment can be minimised by applying chemicals only where and when they are really needed rather than for cosmetic or insurance reasons. This can be aided by the use of forecasting systems, of materials with reduced potential for leaching and of materials which are added at rates of a few grammes per hectare. Similar considerations apply to the use of nitrogen fertilisers although the processes leading to the loss of an individual nitrate molecule added as fertiliser are complex and may take longer than a single season. Losses from fields into ground water represent only part of the potential adverse environment*l impact of farm practices. Pesticides can be lost when sprayers are washed as can animal waste products from intensive housing systems. Such systems represent a source of nutrient loss both from the housed units and when wastes are applied to land organic production systems where the elements of crop and animal husbandry are more tightly coupled may allow reduced nutrient losses. A major series of trials assessing the environmental impact of organic farming has recently been established by SAC.

Farms also influence the environment in terms farm roads, on-farm food processing, eg dairy products witch can produce large volumes of slightly contaminated water, building activities etc. All of these need to be assessed for their environmental impact. Environmental audits are as critical in the rural environment as in the urban environment and can be undertaken as park of SAC Environmental Consultancy Services.

National concerns about the "greenhouse effect" affect farms as well as other enterprises. Farms are accustomed to financial audits of their enterprises and in future audits of the carbon and energy costs of practices and enterprises are likely to be as important. While carbon costs may be relatively easy to calculate with the use of computers, energy balances including those involved in making equipment or building materials, are more complex. Wind generating machines may take longer to come into positive energy balance than is immediately obvious - a point to be considered if set-aside is to be used as the site of small wind farms. The countryside will always be dominated by farming, which must be run as a successful business, but increasingly with emphasis on the environmental consequences of the various financially viable options.

The Scottish Agricultural College.
Bob Smith (Regional Director)
031 668 1921

THE ENVIRONMENT AND THE LAW

by Gerald W. S. Barry W. S.

Formerly the Legal Adviser to the Scottish Landowners' Federation, Gerald Barry is now an Associate with the Edinburgh office of J & F Anderson specialising in Estate, Agricultural and Environmental Law.

The need to protect 'the environment' is high on the list of this Government's priorities which is exemplified by the introduction of the first piece of truly "green legislation" entitled the Environmental Protection Bill which, at the time of writing, is still at Bill stage and has still to complete its final stages through Parliament. The demand for a cleaner environment is no longer voiced by a vocal minority but is now supported by the vast majority of people throughout the U.K. as they see the threat to their quality of life and the countryside through industrial and agricultural pollution with the resulting need for control and proper management. The public is therefore demanding tougher legislation in all areas and this is reflected not only in the U.K. but also in adoption by the European Community of Directives setting standards beyond those currently in place in the U.K. and we are committed not only to transposing them but to enforcing them. It seems that this is just the beginning and it is therefore vital for all those who live and carry on business on the land to realise that protection of the environment will be for the future an essential element in all economic and social policy. For example, the European Commission has adopted internal procedures based on the principle of impact studies, which should enable it to ensure that activities financed by its Regional and Agricultural Funds are compatible with the needs of environmental protection.

Apart from the flow of European legislative measures (the Community, have already introduced well over 100 with major implications for the environment) there is also in place substantial U.K. legislative and regulatory framework over and above the Environmental Protection Bill already referred to. Such measures include the Control of Pollution Act 1974 (as amended with provides inter alia for controls on waste on land, pollution of water, control of noise and pollution of the air and requires the obtaining of consents, licences etc. before discharges, tipping of waste etc. can take place).

The recent Water Act 1989 is also an important measure, for example requiring specific controls over nitrates and the introduction of "nitrate sensitive areas". The Control of Pesticide Regulations, the Control of Substances Hazardous to Health Regulations and the Noise at Work Regulations are good examples of health and safety measures introduced for environmental protection, as well as for the protection of those in the workplace. Conservation of the countryside and of species was the principal purpose of the Wildlife and Countryside Act 1981 and its impact is seen in particular through the designations of Sites of Special Scientific Interest throughout Scotland. There is sufficient space to make reference to only a few of the most important U.K. legislative measures but it can be seen that they are likely to affect very many activities, both business, recreation and leisure, that take place in the countryside.

As already mentioned the European Community is adopting a firm line on the need to protect the environment, viz the recent cases against Britain in the European Court of Justice for infringement of the Directive relating to the quality of water intended for human consumption and for non-compliance with the Directive on the quality of bathing waters. It is clear that the EC accepts the "polluter-pays" principle and this of course is bound to affect consideration of insurance cover and will have important financial repercussions for those who carry on business on the land.

The influence of EC legislation on the U.K. environment must not be underestimated, as it is likely to increase in the run up to the introduction of the Single Market in 1992. We can only look briefly and generally, at what is now taking place, always bearing in mind that EC Directives have to be transposed into U.K. legislation, hence the need for, and the use of, the infringement procedure in cases where Member States do not comply with the requirements of Community Law. It must also now be recognised that European Law is supreme so far as each Member State is concerned. The main recently adopted or outstanding measures relating to the environment fall within the general categories of water protection (quality of drinking and bathing water, nitrate pollution from agricultural operations); air pollution (emissions from vehicles, from industrial plant, that relating to protection of the ozone layer; the production and implication of chlorofluorocarbons (CFCS) into the community are defined by an EC Regulation adopted in April 1990 that seeks to eliminate the use of CFCs by 1997) - it is important to note that an EC Regulation is directly applicable in all Member States and does not require to be confirmed by national Parliaments in order to have binding legal effect an EC Directive which has to be implemented by the national governments normally in the U.K. This takes the form of primary legislation or a Statutory Instrument made under a relevant specific power or an Order under the European Communities Act 1972. A Directive per se does not have binding legal effect unless so implemented. Waste management (new proposals on waste and hazardous waste; a 1989 proposal seeks to harmonise civil liability for damage caused by waste); noise; chemicals and biotechcology; Nuclear safety; and conservation of land and natural resources, flora and fauna. This last category is probably the most significant for land managers and land users. In particular, the influence of the "environmental impact assessment" Directive is likely to be felt most keenly during the planning process where rural projects are involved, as it has been indicated that an assessment of the environmental impact of major agricultural projects will be made compulsory under EC proposals during 1990. A major proposal, in the form of a draft Directive seeking to protect natural and semi-natural habitats and of wild flora and fauna, has been published. When adopted the Directive will constitute the second piece of major Community legislation concerning habitat protection, the other being the 1979 Directive on the conservation of wild birds. Member States will be required to classify "special protection areas" which again is likely to have far reaching implications for planning decisions for the reason that environmental impact assessments are likely to be required for all projects which are located in or are likely to affect the conservation of "a special protection area."

Other matters which have been indicated as likely to be the subject of EC proposals during 1990 are the financing of habitat/biotope projects, protection and development of of grass leys and livestock, such as mixed farms or hill and upland farms will probably find conversion easier than the purely arable unit. This is largely because the stock are present on the farm to provide a ready supply of nutrients initially to keep the system going. With this in mind, many Scottish farms could be well placed to convert in practice although local climatic and nutrient supply and very careful planning of rotation, crop selection, grazing management practices etc are still vital for the practical success of the operation. SAC advisers have local knowledge, can discuss these aspects in detail, and assess the potentials and limitations for particular farm businesses.

Before this stage is reached however, the financial effects of organic farming must be assessed - for most farmers, there must be a financial incentive for making any changes to their commercial businesses and livelihoods!

At the time of writing, there is conjecture that there may be an organic option announced to the proposed Extensification Scheme - this may be in the form of a subsidy to assist with conversion to organic farming, thus possibly making conversion more attractive financially. SAC are able to provide impartial advice both on the financial feasibility of converting to organic farming as well as possible organic rotations, husbandry, systems, marketing etc. Comprehensive laboratory services specific to organic farming are also available.

Careful consideration and planning is needed if you wish to change to an organic system. Do get in touch if we can help.

HOME BANKING

by Ian Duncanson,
Manager, Electronic Business Services, Bank of Scotland
Marketing Department

One dictionary definition of a hob is "a small shelf next to a fireplace on which pans etc may be kept; the top of a stove." In other words, a useful and reliable household item.

Make it plural and you have an even more useful and reliable household item, one that has revolutionised banking and made financial management a simple task. HOBS (Home and Office Banking Service) was pioneered by Bank of Scotland and was the first of its type in Britain.

Basically, it allows you to look after your banking affairs from the comfort of your own home. It is as easy to operate as the remote control of your television set and is a cost-effective way to manage your financial business.

While your bank manager will always be pleased to see you, with HOBS you need never go near your bank branch, which is an important consideration in busy times and when the weather is not at its friendliest.

HOBS uses a fairly simple keyboard which plugs into the back of a screen at one end and the telephone socket at the other. That screen can be your television set, your own personal computer or a stand-alone terminal bought for the purpose.

At the press of a button, the box will dial HOBS and all of your accounts will appear on the screen.

By pressing a few more keys, it is possible to view all your balances, no matter how many Bank of Scotland accounts you might have. You can check up to 600 separate transactions over the last three months without waiting for printed statements.

You can make payments by electronic transfer without writing cheques. Payment can be instructed up to 30 days ahead, with the funds remaining in your account until the payment date. You can thus arrange to have important payments made while you are on holiday, in the full knowledge that they will be taken care of.

Surplus funds can be switched to the Bank's high interest investment account, which pays an attractive rate of interest. Interest is calculated daily to give you maximum return and any transactions made before 5 pm on a business day are effective that day - so that even with overnight deposits you can make money with HOBS.

Thousands of businesses, large and small, throughout the UK are now operating HOBS. The range includes accountants, solicitors, dentists, doctors, shops, tradesmen, insurance brokers, travel agencies, clubs, farmers and grain merchants.

Active cash management can be quite important at a time of high interest rates, particularly to a small firm with substantial sums passing though its account.

You can use HOBS to make payments to employees direct into their bank account, and you can keep tabs on payments that should be made into your account, such as the milk cheques. HOBS operates virtually round the clock and there are no problems with security - it is a highly confidential service using a combination of identity numbers and passwords which will be known only to you or someone authorised by you.

One South West Scotland farmer who uses HOBS admits that he was a bit unsure at the start. He stated: "I struggled to get the video recorder set properly and expected that HOBS would represent another technological challenge but, in fact, I find it easy and enjoyable to operate.

"I feel in total control of my financial affairs and can get things up-to-date when it suits me, usually at the weekends. My wife helps me out in running the business and she has no problem operating HOBS - in fact, it was she who suggested it to me in the first place.

"In the past when things were particularly busy I was liable to let my finances slip and it was beginning to worry me. I had enough on my plate as it was. Now I have established the routine of sitting down and make HOBS work for me."

Bank of Scotland staff will be happy to explain to you how the system operates and to show it in action. This can be done when it suits you at your home - it is, after all, a home banking service.

TAX PITFALLS

by Frank Kidd and Jim Hazelton
Coopers & Lybrand Deloitte

Tax is full of misconceptions, some of which have passed into the realms of mythology. It is a subject which is full of pitfalls; here are a few examples to watch out for:-

1 If you have income tax losses on your farming activities you should be able to set those losses against other income such as interest or rental income. Occasionally the Inland Revenue will argue that after a period of five years such losses may not be used in this way. This rule is predominately to stop "hobby farmers or market gardeners" sheltering other income by carrying out a token farming activity. Unfortunately it is sometimes raised in genuine cases, but you should be able to overcome the problem if you show that the trade is carried on on a commercial basis and with a view to realising profits.

2 The higher the value of your stock at the year end the higher will be your profits and potentially your tax bill. That is not sufficient cause to value your stock as low as possible and there are accounting conventions as to how stock should be valued. In general stock is valued at the lower of cost and realisable value so if what you have is worth less than your costs write that item down at your year end.

As a guide, growing crops are valued at the cost of seeds, fertilisers and sprays plus a proportion of overheads such as labour and machinery costs to date.

Home bred animals are normally valued for convenience as a percentage of market value being 75% for pigs and sheep and 60% for cattle.

3 If you have a production herd and have elected to use the herd basis, then you will be taxable on incidental sales from the herd and receive tax relief for incidental replacements. If you are intending to significantly reduce the size of your herd the magic proportion is 20%; a reduction of less than that amount would be subject to income tax whilst a permanent reduction of greater than that amount will be completely free of tax. Note that the reduction has to be permanent, if within five years you increase that herd again then that will give rise to a tax charge.

4 It is quite normal for tenants of agricultural property to be given the opportunity to buy the land which they occupy at a discount. A problem often arises where the tenant finds it necessary to sell some of the newly acquired land to reduce bank borrowings. Where this happens, the Inland Revenue may seek to subject some or all of the profit on the sale to income tax as trading in land and to make matters worse they may seek to prohibit previous farming losses from being set against that profit. This whole area is complicated and your approach to such a deal should be carefully planned in advance.

5 Many landowners open up bank accounts for young children or transfer or buy shares that produce dividends in the children's names. This is often done to use up the children's personal allowances currently £3,005 per annum. Where the children are unmarried or under 18 this is not effective as the income is treated as that of the parents. This rule however only applies where a parent set up an arrangement, it won't apply if an uncle or a grandparent makes the gift.

6 It is possible to defer capital gains tax on the sale of an asset if the proceeds are reinvested in another qualifying asset. The rules of what is known as rollover relief however are often misunderstood. It applies only where a disposal is treated as a capital and not trading matter and normally only where the old and the new asset are used for purpose of a trade. In addition not all asset qualify for relief, for example shares do not qualify but land, fixed plant and milk quota to qualify. Take care to ensure that the person making the original disposal is the same person reinvesting the proceeds. For example, it is not acceptable for an individual or a partner to sell an asset used in a business and reinvest the proceeds in another asset used perhaps by a company which they own.

7 When you make small part disposals of land not exceeding £20,000 then the capital gains tax effect may be deferred by simply reducing the allowable deduction on the remaining land. This relief, which applies only to small disposals, is preferable to rollover relief on larger disposals because in this case you do not have to reinvest

the proceeds in a new asset and therefore there is a cash flow advantage.

8 As you know, a private dwelling will be exempt from capital gains tax when it is sold if it is an individual's principal private residence. This exemption may be restricted if part of the house has been used exclusively for business purposes, so avoid treating a room say exclusively as an office. Another problem which arises where a partnership owns two farmhouses which are occupied by individual partners is that strictly each partner owns a proportion of both properties rather than a single property outright. The Inland Revenue do not always take this point, but it is as well to arrange matters in such a way so as to avoid this problem.

9 The main way of avoiding inheritance tax is to gift assets to your family and to survive for a period of seven years. Take care however where you do not sever yourself completely from the asset. If you reserve the right to receive any benefit from the asset either by way of use or deriving income from it, then you will not be regarded as having disposed of the asset for inheritance tax and it will still be regarded as belonging to your estate. There are ways of carving out certain rights and then transferring the asset, but again that requires extreme care and proper planning.

10 Many farmers recover VAT from Customs & Excise as they have standard rated costs and zero rated outputs. If that is the case you should consider monthly rather than quarterly returns as this will get your repayments to you that much quicker.

There are now penalties for misdeclarations which include the overstatement of input tax so ensure that your returns are accurate and do not include, for example, input tax on private expenditure.

The letting of bare land was at one time inevitably exempt from VAT if an exclusive licence to occupy was given unless the arrangement was a grazing let, which was often regarded as a zero rated supply. Since 1 August 1989 it has been possible to elect to charge VAT at the standard rate without the tenant's approval and this may improve the recovery of input tax in regard to that land. Watch out though, any such election must cover all agricultural land in the ownership of the person making the election with the exception of that separated by land owned by someone else, or used for a non-agricultural purpose.

Well, there you are, we hope that these thoughts will help to keep your tax affairs on the right track.

S.A.S.C.

The Scottish Agricultural Securities Corporation plc was established in 1933 under the Agriculture Credits (Scotland) Act 1929, for the purpose of granting loans for agriculture in Scotland at a fixed rate. In the early days these loans were made available for the purchase of land only, but in more recent times SASC has widened its aims to embrace the purchase of buildings, forestry and woodlands. Loans are not available for the purchase of livestock or farm equipment.

S.A.S.C. is jointly owned by three of Scotland's leading banks, Bank of Scotland, Clydesdale and The Royal Bank of Scotland. The board consists of four directors, each bank appointing one, along with an independent director, usually a farmer. The current Chairman is one of Scotland's best known agriculturalists, Mr Sandy Inverarity, a past President of the National Farmers Union of Scotland and presently Chairman of the Board of The Scottish Agricultural College. SASC is run by a very small staff and prides itself in the "personal touch". An enquiry will be dealt with promptly by the General Manager, Mr Nigel Richardson, who will then see the deal through to the final settlement of the loan. No problems arise as a result of delays awaiting decision from higher office, an important factor when a short notice closing date is stipulated.

Two types of loans are available, both of which are offered over a period from 10 - 25 years. In each case the minimum amount lent is £15,001.

The Endowment Loan is repaid in two parts. The interest is payable to SASC in the normal manner, whilst the capital is repaid in a lump sum at the end of the loan term, via an approved insurance company, to whom the premiums will have been paid direct.

In the case of the Capital and Interest Loan, both elements are paid to SASC in their entirety over an agreed period.

In each case the interest is fixed at the rate offered at the outset of the loan and payments and repayments to SASC are made half yearly. Both of these factors are seen as beneficial to the client's cash flow.

Depending upon the individual client's circumstances, these loans will normally qualify for tax relief. Prior to taking out an SASC loan, potential clients are advised to discuss this with their professional adviser.

Security required by SASC on land is 2/3 value of the property, including house and appropriate buildings. For a forestry loan the requirement is 2/3 of land value plus 50% of the timber value. Land may not be let out to a tenant during the loan period without the specific consent of SASC.

SASC will only recall a loan under default of payment and records show this to be a very rare occurrence. In no circumstances will the rate of interest agreed at the outset of the loan be altered.

SASC, which operates only in Scotland, has seen much of its increased business in the last few years emanate from farmers south of the border wishing to purchase land here. Having sold their English holding for an inflated price, they then seek to purchase a much larger acreage in Scotland for the same outlay.

SASC regards itself as a most useful and suitable alternative to the more traditional lenders whose interest rates can fluctuate dramatically. SASC's fixed rate of interest is of enormous benefit to the farmer in budgeting and planning ahead, which in these troubled times in the industry is of paramount importance.

"KEEPING THE FARM IN THE FAMILY"

J. McLean

It has always been a fairly high priority amongst farmers, to pass their business on to the next generation. Considerable amounts of time and effort are usually put in to improving the condition of the farm - "to leave it in a better state than when it was taken over." However financial and tax planning has tended to be put off as long as possible. Unless sufficient thought is given to the tax implications of transfers, then the tax man may claim a significant part of the business which the farmer has worked so hard to improve.

Inheritance tax is the latest in a line of taxes on lifetime and death gifts. Inheritance tax was formally introduced by the Finance Act of 1986 as a replacement for Capital Transfer Tax.

Inheritance tax is charged on certain lifetime gifts, on wealth at death and on certain transfers into and out of trusts. The lifetime transfers which are liable to tax are called chargeable transfers. Some lifetime transfers are only liable if the donor dies within seven years of making them. These are called potentially exempt transfers. If the donor survives seven years the potentially exempt transfer, becomes an exempt transfer. If he dies within seven years it becomes a chargeable transfer.

The point at which inheritance tax becomes payable is reached when chargeable transfers exceed £128,000. The tax is then charged at a rate of 40 per cent on any transfer in excess of this value. With the recent rise in property prices, more people are likely to have assets exceeding a value of £128,000 and therefore potentially liable to incur inheritance tax on transfer. Therefore, inheritance tax does not only apply to the obviously wealthy.

Although inheritance tax is charged on assets owned less any liabilities (eg. overdraft, mortgage) the problem can still be particularly acute in farming. Farms tend to have a high capital value, but show a low return on this capital. This means that inheritance tax on farming estates could amount to a considerable sum - a sum which the business would find difficult, and in some cases, impossible to pay, without the sale of the farm.

However, much can be done to mitigate the effects of inheritance tax, provided appropriate action is taken. This involves the use of exempt and potentially exempt transfers.

Exempt transfers can include:

* small gifts to any one person which do not exceed £250 in the tax year.
* gifts on marriage - up to £5000 by a parent, up to £2500 by a grandparent or up to £1000 by any other person - provided it is a lifetime gift made to the couple in consideration of their marriage.
* annual transfers of up to £3000.
* transfers between husband and wife.

Where a transfer is not covered by exemptions, it may not be treated as a chargeable asset in the first instance. In such a case it is referred to as a potentially exempt transfer. It is then only relevant in the calculation of inheritance tax if the donor dies within seven years of making the gift. If death occurs between 3 and 7 years after the gift is made inheritance tax is payable at a reduced rate of between 80 and 20 per cent of the full rate.

The seven year period does not begin until the donor ceases to enjoy any benefit from the gift. Care must therefore be taken to avoid any reservation of benefit from all or part of the gift, eg. parents gifting the farm, including the farmhouse to a son or daughter, but continuing to live in the farmhouse, could be deemed to have reserved benefit from the gift and the whole gift (farm and farmhouse) could remain in the parents estate, until the parents began to pay a market rent for the farmhouse. As an alternative solution the parents could have transferred the ownership of the farm only, but retained the ownership of the farmhouse.

Because most lifetime gifts are now potentially exempt the main examples of chargeable lifetime transfers are those involving companies and certain types of trust. Where inheritance tax is payable on a lifetime transfer into a discretionary trust, the rate is half the death rate ie. 20 per cent.

As well as exemptions, there are the business property and agricultural property reliefs. The rates of relief are 50 per cent or 30 per cent depending on the type of interest held in the business. The same rates apply to agricultural property, 50 per cent if the donor had vacant possession immediately before the transfer (or could obtain it within the next twelve months) and 30 per cent on tenanted agricultural property. Thus a farm worth £500,000 with vacant possession would be written down to £250,000 for inheritance tax purposes. If this farm was equally owned by a husband and wife in partnership it could be passed on free of inheritance tax, depending, of course, on the value of the rest of their assets.

These reliefs are available subject to certain time limitations on the period of ownership. Other conditions may also have to be met.

Trusts are commonly used in estate planning. These can be of particular importance for those with young children or in situations where the donor is unwilling to make unrestricted gifts at a particular point in time.

Planning is crucial if property is to be passed successfully to the next generation, without paying large amounts of inheritance tax. It is much easier to plan effectively, with a high chance of success, if a person is aged 50 rather than 80.

It is also important to update plans in the light of changes in inheritance tax rules, or changes in family circumstances. The steps which will be taken will aim to ensure that property ownership is correctly placed to establish the maximum available reliefs on the date of any assessment.

Where proper planning has not taken place and a will produces undesirable inheritance tax consequences, it is still possible to have the provisions changed by "deed of family arrangement" if all the beneficiaries of the will agree. However this facility may not be available in years to come and, in any case, it makes sense to try to get the planning right in the first place.

By seeking competent professional advice, it can become much easier to "keep the farm in the family."

J. McLean
Senior Farm Business Adviser
S.A.C.

DISEASES WHICH MAY PASS FROM ANIMALS TO PEOPLE – ZOONOSES

The prevention of ill-health caused by farm work is very important and it has been the subject that has tended to take second place to the need to fit safety cabs to tractors and to guard dangerous machinery. Lengthy periods of occupational ill-health, particularly to a farmer without regular labour, can be expensive inconvenient and in some cases may require a change of farming system, at worst it could be fatal. It is important that farmers have knowledge on how the diseases may occur, their effect and how the chance of infection can be prevented.

The following conditions and infections are caused by micro-organisms which are all under the scope of the Control of Substances Hazardous to Health Regulations 1989.

Enzootic Abortion of Ewes

Infection with chlamydia psittaci (non-avian strain) is now common in sheep flocks and is a cause of abortion. Pregnant women infected with this organism may contract severe septiceamia, leading to premature delivery and sometimes loss of the foetus (baby). One woman has died of this disease.

The infecting organisms are present in large numbers in the aborted lamb and afterbirth. These should be disposed of with as little handling as possible and everyone concerned with lambing should be very particular about washing hands, clothing and boots. Although the disease is very rare in humans, the effects can be severe.

Pregnant women should not lamb sheep.

Orf

Orf is a contagious pustular condition in sheep caused by a virus (parapoxvirus). Infections spreads to humans via abrasions or cuts in the skin and causes a blistering swelling. It can heal without treatment but may become infected. Similar lesions can be caused by a pox virus affecting cattle (pseudo-cowpox) known as Milkers Nodes (unlike orf, it can spread from person to person).

Always wash your hands after handling any animal. Cover cuts and abrasions with waterproof plasters. Consult your doctor if the swelling becomes infected.

Ringworm

Ringworm is caused by a fungus which attacks the hard protective layer of the skin, hair and nails (horn, hoofs, feathers). The most common sources of animal ringworm in humans are cattle, cats and dogs. Although animal ringworm is most often seen in children and young adults, any age may be infected. The infection can heal without treatment. However, this may take a long time so it is best to seek medical advice. Anti-fungal creams are usually effective but not always. Therefore if there has been no improvement after 2 weeks of this type of treatment, it may be necessary to take anti-fungal treatment by mouth. Scalp ringworm also requires treatment by mouth. Cats may "carry" the organism without showing signs of infection. It is unusual to "catch" this disease a second time as a person who has been infected tends to develop an immunity which lasts for a long time.

Tetanus

Tetanus is a constant threat to everyone involved in agriculture. In the last few years, several farm workers have died from tetanus. The deaths are preventable.

Cuts and abrasions which are every day occurrences in farming can become contaminated by tetanus spores commonly found in stable and farmyard manure and soil. The spores can multiply in the wound and produce a toxin leading to interference with nervous control of muscle and death from respiratory failure. The most dangerous type of injury is that known as puncture wound such as that made by a nail or a wood splinter. These are of the type which are considered to be trivial and are often untreated and forgotten.

Prevention is the only certain way of dealing with this occupational hazard. All farmers, farm workers and their families should ensure they are protected against the disease. It is recommended that a full immunisation course consisting of three injections (childhood) followed by a booster five years later and a reinforcing dose 5 to 15 years after that. This is considered by doctors to provide a satisfactory degree of protection. A good way of remembering to have a booster is to have it at each "decade", birthday ie 20, 30, 40 etc. Any unprotected individual sustaining an injury should seek medical guidance immediately.

Leptospirosis

There are two types which are important on farms - rat associated (Weil's Disease) and cattle associated (Hardjo). The disease is recognised in cattle by milk drop or abortion or a typical mastitis.

Both rats and cattle pass on the disease by contaminating water, soil and matters such as animal feed with their infected urine. Humans pick up the disease by being in contact with contaminated matter. The organism enters the body through cuts, abrasions, eyes and the lining of the mouth and nose. Milkers who stand in pits may be at particularly high risk. The organism thrives in wet, warm conditions. It cannot long survive drying or salt water. It is killed in chlorine. Cattle associated leptospirosis is often not recognised in humans as the symptoms can easily seem like flu with malaise, aching limbs and slight fever. Symptoms may progress to high fever, severe headache and mental confusion in a few cases.

Important facts still need to be learned about leptospirosis. It is therefore important that this condition is always reported to the Health and Safety Executive as required by the Reporting of Injuries, Diseases and Dangerous Occurrences Regulations (RIDDOR) - which requires all cases of recognised zoonoses to be reported to the HSE. Both types are readily treatable with antibiotics so it is very important to tell your doctor what job you do. If infection is not treated, it can last for months, during which time one feels very lethargic, occasionally it causes meningitis. It is occasionally fatal. Weil's Disease is in general more serious, with jaundice and stiff neck as well as other symptoms.

Normal first aid procedures should be followed, ie cleanse and then cover all cuts, scratches and abrasions with waterproof dressings. Wash hands and forearms before eating, drinking or smoking.

Summary

Awareness of possible risks and dangers is the first line of defence. All diseases and risks are preventable. The family doctor, the veterinary surgeon and the doctors and Agricultural Inspectors in the Health and Safety Executive are some of the sources of information, help and advice which are available.

A DEVELOPMENT IN SHEEP WORMER DELIVERY SYSTEMS

To be effective, anthelmintics must be administered at the correct dose rate, to all susceptible animals, and as part of a well planned worm control strategy.

This has long been the cry of veterinary surgeons and animal health product manufacturers alike, but no more so than in the sheep industry in the last 12 months, where talk of resistance to wormers has made everybody think a little harder.

Whilst millions of sheep are dosed effectively every year, a great many will no doubt receive insufficient wormer for one reason or another. In such circumstances, the wormer is likely to perform less effectively than it should, whatever its chemical group or mode of action.

It is easy to blame flockmasters for failing to gather all their sheep, estimating weights incorrectly, or for forgetting to maintain their drenching gun. But aren't many of the shortcomings associated with poor worming practice a product of the practical pressures of handling and drenching large numbers of sheep?

Surely the animal health product manufacturers have an obligation to make administration of the product as practical and manageable as possible?

With convenience and ease of administration in mind, a new formulation and delivery system of the market leading sheep wormer Systamex* has now been developed by Coopers Pitman-Moore.

The Handipack* system includes a 500ml hip mounted pack, and comes complete with graduated dosing gun. A holster and coiled delivery tube allow the operator complete freedom of movement.

The practical advantages are accentuated by the fact that the active ingredient, oxfendazole, is formulated at a significantly higher concentration than in conventional Systamex drenches. This means one 500ml pack of Systamex Handipack contains enough wormer to treat 100 full grown ewes, or at the other end of the scale, 500 lambs up to 20kg liveweight.

The lower dose volume also means easier administration and less risk of rejection by the sheep.

All this leads to a saving of time and money without compromising the effectiveness of the wormer, enabling the farmer to maximise the return on his investment.

MEETING THE NEEDS
OF THE FARMER, THE CONSUMER
AND THE ENVIRONMENT.
CIBA–GEIGY
SCOTTISH AREA OFFICE
Telephone 031 661 7999

This man just spent £10,000 on a grain dryer he didn't need.

No wonder he's mad.

He'd been producing higher yields for years. He'd had a run of wet harvests. He'd got merchants screaming for low moisture content. And, his old dryer wasn't working properly.

So, he panicked and bought a new one.

What he should have done was contact Hydro-Electric. It's quite possible that one of our farming specialists could have suggested a much more economical solution. Like increasing the air flow in his old machine. Or using a dry air generator.

Or simply altering the operating system.

All of which come a lot cheaper than a dryer.

If you're unhappy with the performance of your grain dryer.

DIAL 100 AND ASK FOR FREEFONE HYDRO-ELECTRIC

You'd be mad not to.

Directory Contents

A man with money to lend...

AGRICULTURAL AND ALLIED WORKERS NATIONAL TRADE GROUP

Headquarters
Headland House, 308 Grays Inn Road, London, WC1X 8DS.
Tel. 071-278-7801
Telex 295239
Fax 071-833-3096

National Secretary
Barry Leathwood.

AGRICULTURAL COLLEGES

The four residential agricultural colleges run by local authorities which teach up to the technician level of qualification are:

Barony College
David Rose—Principal, Parkgate, Dumfries, DG1 3NE.
Tel. 0387-86251

Clinterty Agricultural College
John Telfer—Principal, Kinellar, Aberdeenshire, AB5 0TN.
Tel. 0224-790393

Elmwood Agricultural and Technical College
Norval Black—Principal, Carsiogie Road, Cupar, KY15 4JB.
Tel. 0334-52781

Oatridge Agricultural College
Chris Nixon—Principal, Ecclesmachan, Broxburn, West Lothian, EH52 6NH.
Tel. 0506-854387

THE AGRICULTURAL ENGINEERS ASSOCIATION

Samuelson House, Paxton Road, Orton Centre, Peterborough, Cambridgeshire, PE2 0LT.

Director General
J. Vowles.

SCOTTISH MEMBERS – AGRICULTURAL GUILD OF JOURNALISTS

Charlie Allan.
Arthur Anderson.
George Beck.
Andrew Brown.
Robert Bruce.
Mairi Campbell.
John Duckworth.
Alasdair Fletcher.
Kenneth Fletcher.
Louis Flood.
Claire Footit (A).
Liz Fowler.
John Fraser.
Ronnie Fraser.
Eddie Gillanders
William Howat.
William Howatson.
Graeme Kirk.
Colin Ley.
Douglas Low.
John Lumsden (A).
Angus MacDonald.
Douglas MacSkimming.
Christopher Mackel (Fd).
Fordyce Maxwell.
George Millar (Hon.).
Frieda Morrison.
Ian Morrison.
Ross Muir (A).
Matt Mundell.
Nancy Nicholson.
Ken Rundle.
Patricia Stevenson.
Robin Valentine (Hon.).
Allan Wright (A).

AGRICULTURAL ORGANISATIONS

Animal Diseases Research Association
Moredun Institute, 408 Gilmerton Road, Edinburgh, EH17 7JH.

British Veterinary Association
7 Mansfield Street, London, W1M 0AT.

Hannah Dairy Research Institute
Ayr.

Institute of Auctioneers and Appraisers in Scotland
Secretaries: Messrs Biggart, Baillie and Gifford, 3 Glenfinlas Street, Edinburgh, EH3 6YY.

Macaulay Institute for Soil Research
Craigiebuckler, Aberdeen, AB9 2QJ.

National Institute of Agricultural Engineering (Scottish Station)
Bush Estate, Penicuik, Midlothian, EH26 0HP.

Rowett Research Institute
Bucksburn, Aberdeen, AB2 9SB.

Royal Scottish Agricultural Benevolent Institution
Ingliston, Edinburgh, EH28 8NB

Scottish Agricultural Securities Corporation Ltd
19 Rutland Square, Edinburgh, EH1 2BA

Scottish Agricultural Arbiters' Association
10 Dublin Street, Edinburgh, EH1 3PR.

Scottish Seed and Nursery Trade Association
12 Bruntsfield Crescent, Edinburgh, EH10 4EZ.

AGRICULTURAL TRAINING BOARD (NATIONAL)

Board Headquarters
Stoneleigh Park Pavilion, NAC, Stoneleigh, Kenilworth, Warwickshire, CV8 2UG.

Chairman
John E. Smith.
Deputy Chairman
M.J. Curtis.

Director
D.C. Newman, N.D.A.

ATB SCOTLAND

Headquarters
13 Marshall Place, Perth, PH2 8AH.
Tel. 0738-31481 (3 lines)
Fax. 0738-38208

Director
Michael W. Dean

Depute Director
Jack Kelly

Administrative Officer
Mary Mitchell

Alyth
Andrew Durward Tel. 08283 2641

Aberdeen
Peter Blackhall Tel. 0224 713773

Banff
Graham Hobson Tel. 02612 2063

Dumfries
Ian Gunn Tel. 0387 54315

Edinburgh
David Wright Tel. 031 339 3002

Inveraray
Allan Harper Tel. 0499 2213

Inverness
Arthur MacDonald Tel. 0463 233432

Lanark
Dorothy Douthwaite Tel. 0555 65031

St Boswells
Linda Cassie Tel. 0835 22334

Stirling
Angus Ferguson Tel. 786-71100

Wick
Alan Smurthwaite Tel. 0955 2193

ARCHITECTURAL HERITAGE SOCIETY OF SCOTLAND

(formerly The Scottish Georgian Society)
43B Manor Place, Edinburgh, EH3 7EB.
Tel. 031-225-9724

Contact
Ms M. Gilfillan-Secretary.

ASSOCIATION FOR THE PROTECTION OF RURAL SCOTLAND

14A Napier Road, Edinburgh, EH10 5AY.
Tel. 031-229-1 081

Contact
Robert L. Smith, O.B.E.—Director.

ASSOCIATION OF SCOTTISH DISTRICT SALMON FISHERY BOARDS

39 Palmerston Place, Edinburgh, EH12 5AU.
Tel. 031-220-4055

Contact
Group Captain J.R.C. Proudlock—Secretary

THE ATLANTIC SALMON TRUST LTD

Moulin, Pitlochry, Perthshire, PH16 5JQ.
Tel. 0796-3439

Contact
Rear-Admiral D. J. Mackenzie, C.B.—Director.

BORDER UNION AGRICULTURAL SOCIETY

Showground Office, Springwood Park, Kelso, TD5 8LS.

Secretary and Treasurer
Donald S. MacLaren.
Tel. Kelso (0573) 24188

BOTANICAL SOCIETY OF EDINBURGH (BSE)

Royal Botanic Garden, Inverleith Row, Edinburgh, EH3 5LR.

Tel. 031-552-7171

Contact
Dr Maria Chamberlain—Honorary Secretary.

BRITISH GEOLOGICAL SURVEY – SCOTTISH OFFICE (BGS)

(formerly Institute of Geological Sciences)
Murchison House, West Mains Road, Edinburgh, EH9 3LA.
Tel. 031-667-1000

Contact
Dr R. W. Gallois-Head of Station.

THE BRITISH INSTITUTE OF AGRICULTURAL CONSULTANTS

National Secretary
H. J. Nation, Durleigh House, 3 Elm Close, Campton, Stafford, Bedfordshire, SG17 5PE.

Scottish Secretary
J.D. Macgregor, BSc(Hons), MSc, Laurence Gould Consultants Ltd, 3 Rutland Square, Edinburgh, EH1 2AS.
Tel. 031-229-8741

BRITISH WATERWAYS BOARD SCOTTISH OFFICE

Lowland Waterways Office, Rosebank House, Main Street, Camelon, Falkirk, FK1 4DS.
Tel. 0324-612415

Contact
James Clarke—Countryside Ranger, Forth and Clyde Canal.

BRITISH WOOL MARKETING BOARD

Head Office
Oak Mills, Clayton, Bradford, West Yorkshire, BD14 6JD.
Tel. 0274-882091

Chairman
A. Evans, O.B.E., FRAgS, Caerffynnon, Bryncrug, Tywyn, Gwynedd, LL36 9RE.

Vice-Chairman
J. W. Raine, C.B.E., Old Parks, Kirkoswald, Penrith, Cumbria, CA10 1DY.

Managing Director
M. Grass.

Secretary
Mrs G. Humphries.

BOARD MEMBERS IN SCOTLAND

Regional Members

Southern
J. Elliot, Rawburn, Longformacus, Duns, Berwickshire, TD11 3PG.

Central
J.E. McNaughton, O.B.E., FRAgS, Inverlochlarig, Balquhidder, Lochearnhead, Perthshire, FK19 8PG.

Northern
A.S. Macdonaid, C.B.E., D.L., FRAgS, Torgorm, Conon Bridge, Ross-shire, IV7 8DN.

Appointment by Ministers
Professor G. F. B. Houston, The Department of Political Economy, Adam Smith Building, University of Glasgow, Glasgow, G12 8RT.

Regional Manager
S. Ballinger, British Wool Marketing Board, Avenue K, Ingliston Showground, Newbridge, Midlothian, EH28 8NB.
Tel. 031-333 1033

CENTRAL SCOTLAND COUNTRYSIDE TRUST

Hillhouseridge Farm, Shottskirk Road, Shotts, Lanarkshire, ML7 4JS.
Tel. 0501-22015
Fax. 0501-23919

Contact
Stephen Roderick—Director.
Rebecca Ford—Promotions Officer

The CSCT are an environmental charity committed to improving the landscape of Central Scotland. They were set up in 1985 and have already planted over 4 million trees and established 30 miles of hedgerows.

CENTRE FOR AGRICULTURAL STRATEGY

University of Reading, 1 Earley Gate, Reading, RG6 2AT.
Tel. 0734-318150/51/52/53

Director
Professor J. S. Marsh.

COMMISSION OF THE EUROPEAN COMMUNITIES OFFICE FOR SCOTLAND

7 Alva Street, Edinburgh, EH2 4PH.
Tel. 031-225-2058

COUNCIL FOR SCOTTISH ARCHAEOLOGY (CSA)

Royal Museum of Scotland, York Buildings, 1 Queen Street, Edinburgh, EH2 1JD.
Tel. 031-225-7534

Contact
Gill Harden

COUNTRY LANDOWNERS' ASSOCIATION

16 Belgrave Square, London, SW1X 8PQ.
Tel. 071-235-0511

Director-General
James M. Douglas, C.B.E.

Press Contact
Tamara Strapp.

COUNTRYSIDE COMMISSION FOR SCOTLAND

Battleby, Redgorton, Perth, PH1 3EW.
Tel. 0738-27921

MEMBERS AND PRINCIPAL OFFICIALS

Chairman
J. Roger Carr.

Vice-Chairman
John Arnott.

Members
Professor C.H. Gimingham.
R. B. Cowie.
E. Langmuir.
I. Miller.
R. Cramond.
Q. Brown.
Professor J. C. Smyth.
Mrs S. Harvey.
M. Turnbull.
Dr W. Mutch.
A. W. Henry.

Director
Duncan Campbell.

Assistant Directors
J. Russell Turner.
Jan Fladmark.
Malcolm A. Payne.
William T. Band.
Roderick I. Fairley.

The Commission is the Secretary of State's adviser on matters concerning the provision, development and improvement of facilities for the enjoyment of the Scottish countryside and for the conservation and enhancement of its natural beauty and amenity. The Commission advises local planning authorities about rural planning matters and the provision of recreation facilities in the countryside. The Commission also has a conservation education function and is able to offer grant-aid in respect of the provisions of new recreation facilities such as car parks and picnic sites.

CROFTERS COMMISSION

Office
4/6 Castle Wynd, Inverness, IV2 3EQ.
Tel. 0463-237231

MEMBERS AND PRINCIPAL OFFICIALS

Chairman
H. A. M. MacLean, B.Sc.(Hons.).

Members—Part-time
I.G. Munro, MRCVS.
B.T. Hunter.
D.A. Morrison.
A.I. Macarthur.
P. Morrison.
D. Macdonald.

Secretary
A. Johnston.

Chief Technical Officer
D. Gordon, BSc (Agr).

CROWN ESTATE COMMISSIONERS – SCOTTISH OFFICE

10 Charlotte Square, Edinburgh, EH2 4DR.
Tel. 031-226-7241

Contact
M.J. Gravestock—Crown Estate Receiver for Scotland.

DEPARTMENT OF AGRICULTURE AND FISHERIES FOR SCOTLAND

Head Office
Pentland House, 47 Robb's Loan, Edinburgh, EH14 1TW.
Tel. 031-556-8400 for switchboard.
Tel. 031-244 plus extension for direct line

Secretary
Loudon P. Hamilton, C.B.

Under Secretary
D. J. Essery.

AGRICULTURAL STAFF

Chief Agricultural Officer
J.F. Hutcheson, BSc (Agr), NDA.

Deputy Chief Agricultural Officer
W. A. Macgregor, ARICS, SDA.

Assistant Chief Agricultural Officers
D. Craven, BSc (Agr)., ARICS.
J. G. Muir, BSc (Agr).
J. Hardie, BSc (Agr).
A. Robb, BSc (Agr).
J.I. Woodrow, BSc (Agr).

Chief Surveyor
N. Taylor, FRICS.

Scientific Adviser
Dr T.W. Hegarty, BSc, PhD, Dip Agr Sc.

Chief Agricultural Economist
Dr J.M. Dunn, MA, BLitt, DPhil.

Chief Meat & Livestock Officer
J. Miller.

Chief Food and Dairy Officer
D.J. MacDonald, BA, MREHIS.

ROYAL BOTANIC GARDEN

Regius Keeper
Dr D. Ingram

Assistant Keeper
Dr Mann.

Assistant Chief Veterinary Officer
J.M. Scudamore, BVSc, BSc, MRCVS.

AREA ORGANISATION

Area	Area Office	Address and Telephone Number
Angus/NE Fife	Dundee	Northern College of Education Building, Gardyne Road, Broughty Ferry, DD5 1PE. Tel. 0382-462840
Argyll	Oban	Cameron House, Albany Street, PA34 4AE. Tel. 0631-63071
Borders	Galashiels	Cotgreen Road, Tweedbank, TD1 3SG. Tel. 0896-58333
Clyde/Central	Glasgow	631 Paisley Rd West, G51 1RR. Tel. 041-427-6521
Grampian	Aberdeen	Atholl House, 84-88 Guild Street, AB9 2ZL. Tel. 0224-574567
Highland	Inverness	Government Building, 28 Longman Road, Longman East, IV1 1SF. Tel. 0463-234141
Lothians/ W. Fife	Edinburgh	Government Buildings, Broomhouse Drive, Saughton, EH11 3XD. Tel. 031-556-8400
North Eastern	Keith	33 Balloch Road, AB5 3HN. Tel. 054-22-7697
Northern	Thurso	Strathbeg House, Clarence Street, KW14 7JS. Tel. 0847-63104
Northern Isles	Kirkwall	Tankerness Lane, KW15 1AQ. Tel. 0856-5444
Perth and Kinross	Perth	7 Mill Street, PH1 5HZ. Tel. 0738-21261
Skye/ Western Isles	Portree	Estates Office, IV51 9DH. Tel. 0478-2516
Southern	Dumfries	161 Brooms Road, DG1 3ES. Tel. 0387-55292
South Western	Ayr	Russell House, King Street, KA8 0BE. Tel. 0292-610188

FARMING AND WILDLIFE TRUST LTD – SCOTTISH BRANCH

The Edinburgh School of Agriculture, West Mains Road, Edinburgh EH9 3JG
Tel. 031-667 1041 *or* 0620-83240

Contact
Ken V. Runcie—Scottish Advisor.

FEDERATION OF AGRICULTURAL CO-OPERATIVES (UK) LTD

17 Waterloo Place, Leamington Spa, Warwickshire, CV32 5LA.

Director-General
W.E. Wilson.

FERTILISER MANUFACTURERS' ASSOCIATION LTD

Greenhill House, Thorpe Wood, Peterborough, Cambs., PE3 6GF.

Director-General
B. Higgs.

FISH FARMING

CONTACT POINTS WITHIN SCOTTISH FISH FARMING INDUSTRY

Scottish Salmon Marketing Board
Drummond House, Scott Street, Perth, PH1 5EJ.
(A. Gray).
Tel. 0738-35973

Scottish Salmon Growers'Association
Drummond House, Scott Street, Perth, PH1 5EJ.
(W. Crowe).
Tel. 0738-35420

British Trout Association
PO Box 189, London, SW6 7UT.
(Amanda Courtney).
Tel. 071-385-1158/9

Association of Scottish Shellfish Growers
Tigh Na Speir, Connel, Argyll, PA37 1PH.
(Jarfice McGhee).
Tel. 0631-71-653

Shetland Salmon Farmers'Association
O.I.L. Base, Geemista, Lerwick, Shetland, ZE1 0PY.
(J. Moncrieff).
Tel. 0595-4242

SNFU
Caroline Lang.
Tel. 031-337-4333

Crown Estate Commissioners
10 Charlotte Street, Edinburgh, EH2 4DR.
(M. Gravestock).
Tel. 031-226-7241

Institute of Aquaculture
University of Stirling, Stirling, FK9 4LA.
(Professor R. Roberts—Director).
Tel. 0786-73171

Highlands and Islands Development Board
Bridge House, 27 Bank Street, Inverness, IV1 1 QR.
(Ian Sutherland).
Tel. 04632-34171

FOOD FROM BRITAIN

301-344 Market Towers, New Covent Garden Market, London, SW8 5NQ.
Tel. 071-720-2144
Fax. 071-627 0616

Executive Director
Derek Garner.

FOOD AND DRINK FEDERATION

Federation House, 6 Catherine Street, London, WC2B 5JJ.
Tel. 071-836-2460

Contact
Denis Budge.

GOAT PRODUCERS' ASSOCIATION

RASE, National Agricultural Centre, Stoneleigh, Kenilworth, Warwickshire, CV8 2LZ.
Tel. 0203-696969 (ext 384)

Secretary
Alan Nolan.

HEALTH AND SAFETY EXECUTIVE

314 St Vincent Street, Glasgow, G3 8XG.
Tel. 041-204-2646

Belford House, 59 Belford Road, Edinburgh, EH4 3UE.
Tel. 031-225-1313

Baynards House, 1 Chepstow Place, Westbourne Grove, London, W2 4TF.
Tel. 071-221-0870

Director-General
J.D. Rimington.

HIGHLANDS AND ISLANDS DEVELOPMENT BOARD

Headquarters
Bridge House, 20 Bridge Street, Inverness IV1 1QR.
Tel. Inverness (0463) 234171
Telex 75267
Fax 0463-244469

Chairman
Sir Robert Cowan.

The Board assists a wide range oif land based developments (agriculture, forestry, horticulture, etc). On 1 April 1991 the board changes to become Highlands and Islands Enterprise along with its network of Local Enterprise Companies. All enquiries after 1 April should be made to the same telephone numbers as listed for the Board.

KEY CONTACTS

General Farming Assistance
Enquiry Desk—Inverness 234171 or local HIDB office (see Telephone
Directory).

Marketing Developments
Peter Brown
Tel. Inverness 244239

Area Programmes, Diversification and Policy
Bob Stubbs
Tel. Inverness 244481

HIGHLANDS AND ISLANDS SHEEP HEALTH ASSOCIATION (HISHA)

Chairman
Alastair Swanson, Tister Farm, Halkirk, Caithness
Tel. 0955 86205

Secretary
Norman Logie, 14 Tomich, Beauly, Inverness
Tel. 0463 782634

HISHA is a farmer-led Association which aims to maintain the high health status of sheep in the North of Scotland. Its 900 members participate in a health scheme which provides buyers of breeding sheep with an assurance that sheep purchased are free from Enzootic Abortion of Ewes.

HISTORIC BUILDINGS AND MONUMENTS, SCOTLAND

20 Brandon Street, Edinburgh, EH3 5RA.
Tel. 031-244-3144

HOME-GROWN CEREALS AUTHORITY

Hamlyn House, Highgate Hill, London, N19 5PR.
Tel. 071-263-3391

General Manager and Secretary
C.J. Ames.

USEFUL NAMES AND ADDRESSES — HORTICULTURE

Horticultural Development Council
18 Lavant Street, Petersfield, Hants, GU32 3EW.
Tel. 0730-63736

Secretary
E.J. Kennedy.

Horticultural Trades Association
Horticultural House, 19 High Street, Theale, Reading, Berkshire, RG7 5AH.
Tel. 0734-303132
Institute of Horticulture
Secretary Scottish Branch
P.A. Gill, Scottish Crop Research Institute, Invergowrie, Dundee, DD2 5DA.
Tel. 089-94-288

National Farmers' Union of Scotland
17 Grosvenor Crescent, Edinburgh, EH12 5EN.
Tel. 031-337-4333

Horticultural Secretary
Ronald Crichton.

Oatridge and Clinterly Agricultural Colleges
Ecclesmachan, Broxburn, West Lothian, EH52 6NH.
Tel. 0506-854387

The Scottish Agricultural Colleges Ltd
Oakbank Road, Perth, PH1 1HF.
Tel. 0738-36611

Scottish Agricultural Organisation Society
Claremont House, 18/19 Claremont Crescent, Edinburgh, EH7 2JW.
Tel. 031-556-6574

Contact
Edward Rainy Brown—Chief Executive

THE INSTITUTE OF BREWING

33 Clarges Street, London, WlY 8EE.
Tel. 071-499-8144

INTERVENTION BOARD FOR AGRICULTURAL PRODUCE

Fountain House, 2 Queen's Walk, Reading, RG1 7QW.
Tel. 0734-583626

Chief Executive
G. Stapleton.

INTERNATIONAL SHEEP DOG SOCIETY

64 St Loyes Street, Bedford, MK40 1EZ.
Tel. Bedford 52672

Secretary, Treasurer and Keeper of the Stud Book
A. Philip Hendry.

THE MALTSTERS' ASSOCIATION OF GREAT BRITAIN

Lindpet House, Market Place, Grantham, Lincolnshire, NG31 6LP.

MEAT AND LIVESTOCK COMMISSION

PO Box 44, Winterhill House, Snowdon Drive, Milton Keynes, MK6 1AX.
Tel. 0908-677577
Telex 82227
Fax 0908-609221

Director-General
H.C. Oberst.

Chairman
G. John.

Deputy Chairman
R. W. Mattes.

Marketing Director
G. A. Dobbin.

Director of Planning and Research
G. Harrington.

Technical Director
C. W. Maclean.

Regional General Manager—Scotland
A. Donaldson.

Deputy Regional General Manager—Scotland
A. Downie.

Senior Livestock Officer—Scotland
G. M. McPherson.

Scottish Office
3 Atholl Place, Perth.
Tel. 0738-27401

MINISTRY OF AGRICULTURE, FISHERIES AND FOOD

Whitehall Place, London, SW1A 2HH.
Tel. 071-270-3000

THE MOUNTAINEERING COUNCIL OF SCOTLAND (MCofS)

4E Battery Terrace, Oban, Argyll, PA34 5DN.
Tel. 0631-63878 (home) or 0631-62244 (work).

Contact
Dr John W. Leftley—Honorary Secretary

THE NATIONAL ASSOCIATION OF AGRICULTURAL CONTRACTORS

Huts Corner, Tilford Road, Hindhead, Surrey, GU26 6SF.
Tel. Hindhead (0428 73) 5360.

Secretary
J. L. Taylor.

NATIONAL ASSOCIATION OF BRITISH AND IRISH MILLERS

21 Arlington Street, London, SW1A 1RN.
Tel. 701-493-2521

Director-General
J. Murray.

NATIONAL ASSOCIATION OF SEED POTATO MERCHANTS

Suite 'A', Palmer House, Palmer Lane, Coventry, CV1 1FN.
Tel. 0203-553949

Secretary
A.B.S. Paine

NATIONAL CATTLE BREEDERS' ASSOCIATION

Lowford Grange, Lowford Heath, Long Lowford, Rugby, CV23 9HG.
Tel. 0788-565264
Fax. 0788-67142

Secretary
R. W. Kershaw.

THE NATIONAL FARMERS' UNION OF ENGLAND AND WALES

Agriculture House, Knightsbridge, London, SW1X 7NJ.
Tel. 071-235-5077

Director General
David Evans.

Welsh Office
Agriculture House, 19/21 Cathedral Road, Cardiff, CF1 9LJ.
Tel. Cardiff (0222) 41552/3

Head of Public Affairs
Miss A. Dillon.

THE NATIONAL FARMERS' UNION MUTUAL INSURANCE SOCIETY LTD

Head Office
Stratford-upon-Avon, CV37 7BJ.

Scottish Office
135/143 Bath Street, Glasgow, G2 2SX.
Tel. 041-204-2231

Chairman of Scottish Board
J. A. McIntyre, O.B.E., J.P.

Branch Manager
K. G. Smith, ACII.

Sales Manager (Glasgow)
G. A. K. Taylor, FCII.

Sales Manager (Aberdeen)
W. S. Murdoch, FCII.

Area Offices
Aberdeen: 25 Rubislaw Terrace, Aberdeen.
Tel. 0224-644623
Dumfries: 10-12 Buccleuch Street, Dumfries.
Tel. 0387-56754
Edinburgh: 12 Castle Terrace, Edinburgh.
Tel. 031-229-8263.
Inverurie: Thainston Agricultural Centre, Inverurie, AB5 9NT.
Tel. 0467-25424
Kelso: 66 Woodmarlet, Kelso, TD5 7AX.
Tel. 0573-25177
Nairn: 8 St Ninian Road, Nairn, IV12 4EQ.
Tel. 0667-54295
Perth: 28 York Place, Perth.
Tel. 0738-25517
Thurso: 55 Scapa House, Thurso, Caithness, KW14 7JX.
Tel. 0847-65005

SCOTTISH BOARD OF DIRECTORS

General Directors
J. A. McIntyre, O.B.E., J.P., Glenorchy, Broadstone Road, Stranraer, Wigtownshire, DG9.
I. D. Grant, C.B.E., FRAgS, Thorn, Alyth, Perthshire, PH11 8NP.

Local Directors
J. Caldwell, Moorfield, Kilmarnock, Ayrshire, KA2 0AH.
A.R. Campbell, Cuil, Castle Douglas, Kirkcudbrightshire, DG7 2BS.
D.M. Cargill, Coldstream, Laurencekirk, Kincardineshire, AB3 1BX.
J. Fleming, Hailhill, Crossford, Carluke, Lanarkshire, ML8 5QH.
J. B. Forrest, FRAgS, Craigswalls, Duns, Berwickshire, TD11 3PZ.
H. A. M. Fraser, J.P., Dunain Mains, Inverness, IV3 6JX.
J. E. Jeffrey, Beilgrange, Dunbar, East Lothian, EH42 1SY.
W. Lammie, Low Glenstockadale Farm, Leswalt, Stranraer, Wigtownshire, DG9 0LT.
J. E. McNaughton, O.B.E., Inverlochlarig, Balquhidder, Lochearnhead, Perthshire, FK19 8PQ.
R. N. L. Malcolm, D.L., J.P., Duntrune Castle, Lochgilphead, Argyll, PA31 8QQ.
J. M. Mathieson, O.B.E., D.L., J.P., Inchmagrannachan, Dunkeld, Perthshire, PH8 0JS.
D. M. Miller, Billster Mains, Wick, Caithness.
A. Taylor, Boghead, Ord, Banff.
W. C. Taylor, Baldoukie, Tannadice, Forfar, Angus, DD8 3SN.
I. J. Turnbull, BSc, Boghall, Kingsbarns, St Andrews, Fife, KY16 8QA.

NATIONAL OFFICE OF ANIMAL HEALTH

3 Crossfield Chambers, Gladbeck Way, Enfield, Middlesex, EN2 7HF.

NATIONAL PIG BREEDERS' ASSOCIATION

Rickmansworth Road, Watford, Herts, WD1 7HE.
Tel. 0923-343-77

Chief Executive
Grenville Welsh.

NATIONAL TRUST FOR SCOTLAND

5 Charlotte Square, Edinburgh, EH2 4DU.
Tel. 031-226-5922

Contact
Paul Johnson—Chief Ranger

NATIONAL SHEEP ASSOCIATION

The Sheep Centre, Malvern, Worcs., WR13 6PH.
Tel. 0684-892661
Fax 0684-892663

Contact
John Thorley

NATURE CONSERVANCY COUNCIL — SCOTTISH HEADQUARTERS (NCC)

12 Hope Terrace, Edinburgh, EH9 2AS.
Tel. 031-447-4784

Contact
Charles McPhail—Senior Information Officer.

NORTH OF SCOTLAND MILK MARKETING BOARD

Claymore House, 29 Ardconnel Terrace, Inverness, IV2 3AF.
Tel. 0463-232611

Managing Director
J.A. Anderson.

THE ORGANIC GROWERS' ASSOCIATION

86 Colston Street, Bristol, BS1 5BB.
Tel. 0272-299800

Contact
Nigel Dudley.

PLUNKETT FOUNDATION FOR CO-OPERATIVE STUDIES

23 Hanborough Business Park, Long Hanborough, Oxford, OX7 2LH.
Tel. 0993-883636
Fax. 0993-883576

Contact
Mrs N. C. Colley.

POTATO MARKETING BOARD

Head Office
50 Hans Crescent, Knightsbridge, London, SW1X 0NB.
Tel. 071-589-4874

Scottish Divisional Office
H.B. Edmond, 8 Manor Place, Edinburgh, EH3 7DF.
Tel. 031-225-1466

Scottish Area Offices
Perthshire, Fife, Kinross, Clackmannan
P. Read, 53 York Place, Perth, PH2 8EH.
Tel. 0738-22305

Argyll, Ayrshire, Berwick, Bute, Dumfries, Dunbartonshire, Islands off Argyll, Kirkcudbright, Lanarkshire, Lothians, Peebles, Renfrew, Roxburgh, Selkirk, Stirling, Wigtown
H.D.D. Yates, 8 Manor Place, Edinburgh, EH3 7DF.
Tel. 031-225-1466

Aberdeen, Banff, Caithness, Hebrides, Inverness, Islands off Inverness, Islands off Ross, Moray, Nairn, Orkney, Ross, Shetland, Sutherland.
D.G. MacKenzie, 2nd Floor, Thainstone Agricultural Centre, Inverurie, Aberdeenshire, AB5 9WT
Tel. 0467 25408

Angus, Kincardine
A.C.L. Comrie, Mansfield, Coutties Wynd, Forfar, DD8 2EX.
Tel. 0307-62391

Scottish Publicity Office
Mrs S.A. Stein, 8 Manor Place, Edinburgh, EH3 7DF, Tel. 031-225 1466

RAMBLERS ASSOCIATION (SCOTLAND)

Kelinbank, Freuchie, Fife, KY7 7EP.

Contact
Dave Morris—Scottish Officer

RARE BREEDS SURVIVAL TRUST

4th Avenue, National Agricultural Centre, Stoneleigh Park, Kenilworth, Warwicks, CV8 2LG.
Tel. 0203-696551

Contact
Mrs P. Cassidy.

RED DEER COMMISSION

Knowsley, 82 Fairfield Road, Inverness, IV3 5LH.
Tel. 0463-231751

Contact
G. Motion—Assistant Secretary.

ROYAL AGRICULTURAL SOCIETY OF ENGLAND

National Agricultural Centre, Stoneleigh, Warwickshire, CV8 2LZ.
Tel. 0203-696969

Chief Executive
Robin Hicks.

ROYAL ASSOCIATION OF BRITISH DAIRY FARMERS

55 Sleaford Street, London, SW8 5AB.
Tel. 071-627-2111

Chief Executive
Philip Gilbert.

ROYAL COMMISSION ON THE ANCIENT AND HISTORICAL MONUMENTS OF SCOTLAND

54 Melville Street, Edinburgh, EH3 7HF.
Tel. 031-225-5994

Contact
R.J. Mercer—Secretary.

THE ROYAL HIGHLAND AND AGRICULTURAL SOCIETY OF SCOTLAND

Edinburgh Exhibition and Trade Centre, Ingliston, Edinburgh, EH28 8NF.
Tel. 031-333 2444

OFFICE-BEARERS 1990-91
President
Col. B.M. Knox, MC, TD, Martnaham Lodge, Ayr, KA6 6ES.

Vice-Presidents
W. Goldie, Barassie Farm, Troon, Ayr, KA10 7HT.
The Rt. Hon. Lord Goold, CA, DL, Sandyknowe, Waterfoot, Clarkston, Glasgow, G76 8RN.
Sir Eric Yarrow, MBE, DL, Cloak, Kilmacolm, Renfrewshire, PA13 4SD.
C. Young, Rosemount, West Port, Lanark, ML11 1TJ.

Chairman of Board of Directors
R.J. Forrest, Preston, Duns, Berwickshire, TD11 3TQ.

Chairman Designate
J.A. Sleigh, West Fingask, Oldmeldrum, Inverurie, Aberdeenshire, AB5 0EA

Hon Secretary
C.I.M. Gair, BSc (Agric), Easter Moniack, Kirkhill, Inverness, IV5 7PP.

Hon Treasurer
D. Goldie, Longbridgemuir, Clarencefield, Dumfries, DG1 4NA.

CHIEF OFFICIALS
Chief Executive
J.D.G. Davidson, O.B.E., M.B.O., FBIM, FRAgS.

Secretary
J.R. Good.

Accountant and Treasurer
J.M. Arthur, BSc, CA.

ROYAL INCORPORATION OF ARCHITECTS IN SCOTLAND

15 Rutland Square, Edinburgh, EH1 2BE.
Tel. 031-229-7205/7545

Contact
Charles McKean—Secretary.

ROYAL INSTITUTION OF CHARTERED SURVEYORS IN SCOTLAND

9 Manor Place, Edinburgh, EH3 7DN.
Tel. 031-225-7078

Contact
Dawn Buttons—Assistant Secretary.

THE ROYAL SCOTTISH AGRICULTURAL BENEVOLENT INSTITUTION

Ingliston, Edinburgh, EH28 8NB.
Tel. 031-333-1023

President
His Grace the Duke of Buccleuch and Queensberry, KT, VRD.

Secretary
Ian G. Cumming.

THE ROYAL SOCIETY FOR THE PROTECTION OF BIRDS

RSPB Press Office
The Lodge, Sandy, Bedfordshire, SG19 2DL.
Tel. Sandy (0767) 680551 or Sandy (0767) 89298 (after 5.15 pm)
Fax. 0767-292365

Scotland
17 Regent Terrace, Edinburgh, EH7 5BN.
Tel. 031-557-3136

Information Officer
David Mitchell.
Tel. Home: 031-558-1974

SALTIRE SOCIETY

9 Fountain Close, High Street, Edinburgh, EH1 1TF.
Tel. 031-556-1836

Contact
Kathleen Austin—Secretary.

SCOTLAND'S GARDENS SCHEME

31 Castle Terrace, Edinburgh, EH1 2EL.
Tel. 031-229-1870

Contact
Mr R. St Clair-Ford—General Organiser.

THE SCOTTISH AGRICULTURAL COLLEGE

The Scottish Agricultural College, Central Office
Cleeve Gardens, Oakbank Road, Perth, PH1 1HF.
Tel. 0738-36611
Fax. 0738-27860

The Scottish Agricultural College, Edinburgh
West Mains Road, Edinburgh, EH9 3JG
Tel. 031-667 1041
Fax. 031-667-2601

The Scottish Agricultural College, Aberdeen
581 King Street, Aberdeen, AB9 1UD
Tel. 0224 480291
Fax. 0224-491989

The Scottish Agricultural College, Auchincruive
Auchincruive, Ayr, KA6 5HW
Tel. 0292 520331
Fax. 0292-521119

ADVISORY OFFICES

Ayr
20 Miller Road, Ayr, KA7 2BQ
Tel. 0292 264627

Balivanich
Balivanich, Isle of Benbecula, PA88 5LA
Tel. 0870 2336

Campbeltown
12 Burnside Street, Campbeltown, Argyll, PA28 6JE
Tel. 0586 52502

Cupar
Parkhouse, 33 Castle View, Cupar, KY15 4DB
Tel. 0334 54055
Fax. 0334 52327

Dumfries
St Mary's Industrial Estate, Dumfries, DG1 1DX
Tel. 0387 61172
Fax. 0387 50028

Edinburgh
Glenbourne, 42 South Oswald Road, Edinburgh, EH9 2HH
Tel. 031-668 1921
Fax. 031-667-7368

Elgin
15 Hay Street, Elgin, IV30 1NQ
Tel. 0343 48787

Forfar
77 North Street, Forfar, DD8 3BL
Tel. 0307 64033

Inverness
Drummondhill, Stratherrick Road, Inverness, IV2 4JZ
Tel. 0463 233266
Fax. 0463 236579

Inverurie
Thainstone Agricultural centre, Inverurie, AB5 9WU
Tel. 0467 25385
Fax. 0467 23777

Keith
Laurelbank, 14 Banff Road, Keith, AB5 3HA
Tel. 054 22 2316/7

Kirkwall
66 Junction Road, Kirkwall, KW15 1AR
Tel. 0856 2698

Lanark
57 High Street, Lanark, ML11 7LF
Tel. 0555 2562
Fax. 0555 3166

Lerwick
Brentham House, Harbour Street, Lerwick, ZE1 0LS
Tel. 0595 3520

Oban
Glencruitten Road, Oban, Argyll, PA34 4DW
Tel. 0631 63093

Paisley
111 Abercorn Street, Paisley, PA3 4AT
Tel. 041-889 9151

Perth
Cleeve Gardens, Oakbank Road, Perth, PH1 1HF
Tel. 0738 36611
Fax. 0738 27860

Portree
The Green, Portree, Isle of Skye, IV51 9BT
Tel. 0478 2993

St Boswells
Greycrook, St Boswells, Roxburghshire, TD6 0EU
Tel. 0835 23322

Stirling
The Alpha Centre, Stirling University, Innovation Park, Stirling, FK9 4NF
Tel. 0786 50964
Fax. 0786 51030

Stonehaven
21 Evan Street, Stonehaven, AB3 2EQ
Tel. 0569 62305

Stornoway
17 Francis Street, Stornoway, PA87 2NB
Tel. 0851 3103

Stranraer
99 George Street, Stranraer, DG9 7JP
Tel. 0776 2649

Thurso
15 Traill Street, Thurso, KW14 8EJ
Tel. 0847 62719

Turriff
Clifton Road, Turriff, AB5 7DY
Tel. 0888 63333/4

VETERINARY INVESTIGATION CENTRES

Aberdeen
Mill of Craibstone, Bucksburn, Aberdeen, AB2 9TS
Tel. 0224 712781
Fax. 0224 715106

Ayr
Auchincruive, Ayr, KA6 5AE
Tel. 0292 520318
Fax. 0292 521069

Dumfries
St Mary's Industrial Estate, Dumfries, DG1 1DX
Tel. 0387 67260
Fax. 0387 50028

Edinburgh
Bush Estate, Penicuik, Midlothian, EH26 0QE
Tel. 031-445 5544
Fax. 031-445 5633

Inverness
Drummondhill, Stratherrick Road, Inverness, IV2 4JZ
Tel. 0463 243030
Fax. 0463 711103

Perth
Cleeve Gardens, Oakbank Road, Perth, PH1 1HF
Tel. 0738 29167
Fax. 0738 43198

St Boswells
Greycrook, St Boswells, Roxburghshire, TD6 0EU
Tel. 0835 22456
Fax. 0835 23643

Thurso
Janetstown, Thurso, KW14 7XF
Tel. 0847 62602
Fax. 0847 66355

SCOTTISH AGRICULTURAL ORGANISATION SOCIETY LTD

Claremont House, 19 Claremont Crescent, Edinburgh, EH7 4JW.
Tel. 031-556 6574
Telex 727124-SAOSUF G
Fax 031-557 3060

Secretary and Chief Executive
E. Rainy Brown.

Finance Manager
J.Y. Donnan, CA.

Development Manager
J. Graham.

Development Executives
J. Anderson, 86 Rutherford Folds, Inverurie, Aberdeenshire
M. R. Burnett, Pulrossie, Dornoch, Sutherland
A. Green, 18/19 Claremont Crescent, Edinburgh, EH7 4JW.
D. Rennie, 18/19 Claremont Crescent, Edinburgh, EH7 4JW.

COUNCIL

President
D. M. Cargill, Park House, Coldstream, Laurencekirk, Kincardineshire.

Vice-President
H. McK. Galloway, The Quarter, New Luce, Wigtownshire.

Council

A.R. Manson, Kilblean, Oldmeldrum, Aberdeenshire.
W.W. Watson Peat, CBE, JP, Carbro, 61 Stirling Road, Larbert, Stirlingshire.
J.A. Henderson, Scrabster House, Thurso, Caithness.
I. Duncan Millar, Tirinie, Aberfeldy, Perthshire.
I. Marr, Cultercullen, Udny Station, Aberdeenshire.
I.C. Weir, Managing Director, United Farmers Ltd, 18/19 Claremont Crescent, Edinburgh, EH7 4JW.
J.P. Fraser, General Manager, West Highland Crofters and Farmers Ltd, Combie Street, Oban, Argyllshire.
G. Whitehead, General Manager, Aberdeen Grain Ltd, Whiterashes, Newmachar, Aberdeen, AB1 8PL.
R.I. Scott, General Manager, Central Farmers Ltd, Aberhill Works, Methil, Fife.
J.L. Goodfellow, Cairnton House, Arbroath, Angus.
Ms Janet Church, Tigh-Na-Speir, Connel, Argyllshire.
H. McK. Galloway, The Quarter, New Luce, Wigtownshire.
J.M. Sharp, Newbigging Walls, Lauder, Berwickshire.
S. Campbell, O.B.E., Cairntradlin, Kinellar, Aberdeen.
J.G. Dunlop, Bishopton Farm, Kirkcudbright.
R. Simpson, Duchiage Farm, Crieff.
J. Playfair-Hannay, Morebattle, Tafts, Kelso, Roxburghshire, TD5 8AD.
J. Don, Freefield, Old Rayne, Insch, Aberdeenshire.
D. Rose, The Barony College, Parkgate, Dumfries, DG1 3NE
S. Cannon, Kames Fish Farming, Kilmelford, Oban, Argyll, PA34 4XA.

SCOTTISH AGRICULTURAL WAGES BOARD

Chairman
R. A. Bennett, C.B.E., Q.C., Pentland House, 47 Robb's Loan, Edinburgh, EH14 1TW.
Home address: 'Laxamyri', 46 Cammo Road, Edinburgh, EH4 8AP.
Tel. 031-339-6111

Secretary
Mrs Sandra A. Cranford, Pentland House, 47 Robb's Loan, Edinburgh, EH14 1TW.
Tel. 031-244-6392 and 6395

Employers' Representatives
D. R. H. Crichton, Assistant Secretary, National Farmers' Union of Scotland, 17 Grosvenor Crescent, Edinburgh, EH12 5EN.
Tel. 031-337-4333
D.A. Hinton, Fulfordlees, Cockburnspath, Berwickshire.
E.J. Stephen, Lower Thorneybank Farm, Rothienorman, Aberdeenshire.
F.R. Evans, Penkiln, Garlieston, Newton Stewart, Wigtownshire.
J. Kinloch, Clathybeg, Gask, Crieff, Perthshire.
R.J. Lennox, O.B.E., J.P., Shemore, Luss by Alexandria, Dunbartonshire.

SCOTTISH ASSOCIATION OF AGRICULTURE

Scottish Office 1978
Edinburgh Exhibition and Trade Centre, Ingliston, Edinburgh, EH28 8NB.
Tel. 031-333-3805

Contact
Dorothy Amyes-Scottish Executive.

SCOTTISH ASSOCIATION OF YOUNG FARMERS' CLUBS

Young Farmers' Centre
Ingliston, Edinburgh, EH28 8NE.
Tel. 031-333-2445

President
W. Rae.

Vice-President
J. Goldie.

Director
J. Kerr, CA.

The Association consists of affiliated Young Farmers' Clubs in Scotland. Objects of this Association of 6,500 members are:

(a) To further the cultural education and training of young people; to promote their knowledge of country life; to create a fuller realisation of the duties and responsibilities of citizenship; and to ensure a greater interest and efficiency in agriculture in all its branches.

(b) To make rural life more attractive to the young members of the community by providing social amenities and facilities for healthy recreation.

(c) To co-operate with Colleges of Agriculture, local Education Authorities and other bodies interested in rural activities and education.

(d) To promote the formation of new clubs and the co-ordination of existing clubs.

(e) To promote international understanding and well-being through
contacts with similar organisations throughout the world.

Motto
Better farmers, better countrymen, better citizens.

COUNCIL

Chairman
A. Peddie, Cornceres Farm, Anstruther, Fife.

Vice-Chairmen
J. Clark, Summerston Farm, Balmore Road, Glasgow.
B. Arnot, Kilmux Farm, Leven, Fife.

FIELD STAFF

National
Margaret Whiteford, Young Farmers' Centre, Ingliston, Edinburgh, EH28 8NE.

East Area
Miss Liza Quilietti, ,Young Farmers' Centre, Ingliston, Edinburgh, EH28 8NE.

North Area
Miss Linda Fraser, 19 Queen Street, Inverness.

West Area
Miss Jane. Currie, 6 Cadzow Street, Hamilton.

Scotland: Scottish Skills Testing Service
Young Farmers' Centre, Ingliston, Edinburgh, EH28 8NE.
Tel. 031-333 2040

SCOTTISH BEEKEEPERS' ASSOCIATION (SBA)

44 Dalhousie Road, Kilbarchan, Strathclyde, PAl0 2AT.
Tel. 05057-2680

Contact
David Blair-Publicity Convener.

SCOTTISH CASHMERE PRODUCERS' ASSOCIATION LTD

Macaulay Land Use Research Institute, Pentlanfield, Roslin, Midlothian, EH25 9RF.
Tel. 031-445-3401
Fax 031-445-4035

Executive Officer
Robert F. Gray.

SCOTTISH CIVIC TRUST

24 George Square, Glasgow, G2 1EF.
Tel. 041-221-1466/7

Contact
Sadie Douglas—Administrative Officer

SCOTTISH COUNTRY LIFE MUSEUMS TRUST LTD

c/o National Museums of Scotland, York Buildings, Queen Street,
Edinburgh, EH2 1JD.
Tel. 031-225-7534

Contact
Gavin Sprott—Secretary.

SCOTTISH CROFTERS' UNION (SCU)

Old Mill, Broadford, Isle of Skye, Inverness-shire, IV49 9AQ.
Tel. 04712-529

Contact
James Hunter—Director.

The SCU has over 4,000 members in over 50 branches throughout the Highlands and Islands; it is run by crofters and works for crofters and for crofting by:

- —ensuring that the case for crofting is put strongly and effectively to government, the EEC and to official agencies;
- —taking up issues affecting crofters and getting them settled in favour of crofters;
- —publicising and promoting the crofting point of view;
- —developing forward-looking and constructive policies for the future of crofting;
- —uniting crofters everywhere in defence of the agricultural and other support services needed to maintain viable and worthwhile crofting communities.

Members can benefit from the SCU's free legal advisory service on crofting
matters and the services of the NFU Mutual Insurance Society; they also have
access to the union's discount scheme on a wide range of purchases.

SCOTTISH CROP RESEARCH INSTITUTE

Invergowrie, Dundee, Tayside, DD2 5DA.
Tel. 0382-562731

Contact
Professor J.R. Hillman—Director.

SCOTTISH DEVELOPMENT AGENCY

Promoting Agricultural Enterprise

The Role of the Scottish Development Agency

The search for ways of increasing the income obtained by farmers from commercial activities is the underlying interest of that umbrella term 'farm diversification'.

Applied narrowly, the term envisages the use by farmers of under-utilised farm assets to start up non-agricultural activities. The Scottish Development Agency has for its part taken a wider view.

The Agency's perspective is that for farming to prosper in a market environment, initiative in a number of areas will be necessary. Farming will have to:—
- —emphasise quality in production
- —market effectively
- —be cost-efficient, particularly through improved business management
- —innovate both in production systems and the range of produce
- —exploit non-agricultural opportunities to add to total farm income.

The SDA has addressed the issue of which bodies are best placed to promote this range of activity. By working to strengthen the capacity of relevant bodies who are both close to farming and who share the objective of promoting a self-supporting industry, the SDA has been able to ensure that new initiatives are appropriately led.

Working with relevant partners, projects are now promoted at both the national and local levels.

SDA interest in the innovation process is to bring viable new production systems into commercial application. Often this is associated with assisting the introduction on a commercial basis of new types of non-surplus produce. An illustration of this is the Scottish Cashmere Project, in which the SDA and the European Commission are sponsoring a breeding programme to expand the availability of cashmere goats in Scotland.

Developing the markets for Scotland's agricultural produce is crucial to the future fortunes of the farming industry. The SDA is assisting the industry to increase its market share and the margins obtained in key markets through a number of market development initiatives. The cornerstone of such initiatives is the interest in enhancing the reputation and protecting the quality of the Scottish product. The Scotch Lamb Initiative and the Scottish Pig Initiative are the latest of such ventures developed by the SDA in partnership with the industry.

Innovation and market development are not unrelated. How they can combine is demonstrated in the Organic Farming Project at Jamesfield Farm, near Newburgh. A partnership involving Safeways, the Scottish Agricultural College and the SDA is involved in supporting this project, which is assessing how organic production systems can be commercially developed at full farm scale.

Whereas the Agency's Food and Agribusiness Division has taken the lead in national developments, local initiatives promoted by the Agency's Regional Directorates have been developing apace in recent years.

Such area initiatives in particular are concerned with promoting the development of local opportunities. Highlighting these opportunities and co-ordinating the provision of information and assistance to the local farming industry are central to these ventures.

The North-West Fife Rural Initiative is a pace-setter in local co-operation. The partners to this initiative (the SDA, Scottish Agricultural College, the local authorities and the private sector bodies) have progressively identified opportunities in farm tourism, property conversion, food processing, etc. and have been able to pool resources to assist local development.

Taking this approach forward, the SDA is a partner with the Scottish Agricultural College in launching a pilot 'Rural Gateway' project to promote diversification and assist the co-ordination of services delivery in the Galloway area. This project is attracting European Commission support at the only project in the UK being funded in their pilot Carrefour programme to improve the information available to the rural sector on economic development opportunities.

Ventures in promoting co-operation between farm businesses themselves are not neglected. The SDA, with the Scottish Agricultural Organisation Society as the development partner, are assisting the growth of agricultural machinery rings on a farming region basis. The SDA's support package is providing rings with computer and accounting software and training with Food from Britain assisting ring manager salary costs.

When it replaces the SDA in April 1991, Scottish Enterprise will be assessing how it can take forward this involvement. Furthermore, it will give considerable local focus to these efforts through the establishment of Local Enterprise Companies which will deliver, under contract to Scottish Enterprise, a wide range of services and schemes currently managed by both the Training Agency and the SDA.

Contact addresses of the SDA regional offices are given below. The Agency's regional network will continue to have responsibility for rural development activities until these are passed on to Local Enterprise Companies, with the advent of Scottish Enterprise (see below).

REGIONAL OFFICES

Borders
Wheatlands Road, Galashiels, TD1 2HQ.
Tel. 0896 58991

Dumfries and Galloway
16 Buccleuch Street, Dumfries, DG1 5AH
Tel. 0387 54444

Fife
441 High Street, Kirkcaldy, KY1 2SX.
Tel. 0592 205171

Glasgow and Strathclyde North
120 Bothwell Street, Glasgow, G2 7JP.
Tel. 041-248-2700

Grampian
10 Queen's Road, Aberdeen, AB1 6YT.
Tel. 0224 641791

Lanarkshire
Rowantree House, Newhouse, Motherwell, ML1 5RX.
tel. 0698 732637

Central
Stirling University Innovation Park, Alpha Centre, Stirling, FK9 4NF.
Tel. 0786 70080

Lothian
Rosebery House, Haymarket Terrace, Edinburgh, EH12 5EZ.
Tel. 031-337 9595

Strathclyde West and South
Merlin House, Mossland Road, Hillingtod Industrial Estate, Glasgow, G52 4XZ.
tel. 041-882 6288

Tayside
Nethergate Centre, Yeaman Shore, Dundee, DD1 4BU.
Tel. 0382 29122

The following core services of the SDA currently carry responsibilities of particular relevance to business development in rural areas.

Rural Development Unit
— provides a central research, planning and liaison function for rural development.

Rosebery House, Haymarket Terrace, Edinburgh, EH12 5EZ.
Tel. 031-337 9595

Scottish Resources Group
— within this Group, there are three Divisions which provide a contact point for business development, planning and research commercialisation in the traditional Scottish industries. The sectors on which they focus are Food and Agribusiness, Scottish Products and Healthcare. The address is:

120 Bothwell Street, Glasgow, G2 7JP.
Tel. 041-248-2700

Tourism and Leisure Division
— co-ordinates and furthers the Agency's activities in the development of tourism and leisure in Scotland.

120 Bothwell Street, Glasgow, G2 7JP.
Tel. 041-248-2700

Crafts Division
— administers a scheme of business development grants and offers support towards training schemes for those involved with crafts.

Rosebery House, Haymarket Terrace, Edinburgh, EH12 5EZ.
Tel. 031-337 9595

EuroInfo Centre
— provides information and advice to businesses about the European Community enabling them to prepare for the Single European market in 1992
— assists small and medium-sized firms to prepare for 1992

120 Bothwell Street, Glasgow, G2 7JP.
Tel. 041-248-2700

Small Firms Information Service
— provides an information and business counselling service to help owners and managers of small businesses with their plans and problems.
— acts as an advisory service to those thinking of starting their own business.

120 Bothwell Street, Glasgow, G2 7JP.
Tel. 041-248-2700

In July 1989, the Secretary of State for Scotland set out his proposals to merge the Scottish Development Agency with the Training Agency to form Scottish Enterprise. Scottish Enterprise will consist of a central statutory body and a network of 13 private, independent local enterprise companies (operating under contract to the central body) which together will carry out the current economic development and environmental functions of the SDA and the training and the enterprise functions of the Training Agency. Scottish Enterprise will be formally established by April 1991.

The services of the Scottish Development Agency which are listed above will continue to be available in the new organisation. Scottish Enterprise's Head Office will be located at:

120 Bothwell Street, Glasgow, G2 7JP.
Tel. 041-248-2700

At the time of writing, the addresses of the local enterprise companies are not known. Listed below are the names of the thirteen LECs:—

Enterprise Ayrshire
Scottish Borders Enterprise Ltd
Dumfries & Galloway Enterprise Co
Fife Enterprise
Forth Valley Enterprise
Glasgow Development Agency
Grampian Enterprise Trust
Lanarkshire Enterprise
Lothian & Edinburgh Enterprise Ltd
Moray, Badenoch & Strathspey Enterprise Company
Renfrewshire Enterprise Company
Scottish Enterprise Tayside

SCOTTISH FISHERMENS' ORGANISATION

Brahead, 601 Queensferry Road, Edinburgh, EH4 6EA.
Tel. 031-339-7972

SCOTTISH HYDRO-ELECTRIC PLC

For help with crop conservation and storage, animal environment, lighting, heating, pumping, irrigation and all other aspects of electricity usage and supply.

CONTACT ADDRESSES:

Highland Area
High Street, Elgin, IV30 1JE.
Tel. 0343 3441

Aberdeen Area
Millburn Street, Aberdeen, AB9 2GT.
Tel. 0224 589999

Southern Area
Dudhope Crescent Road, Dundee, DD1 9DJ.
Tel. 0382 25141

SCOTTISH LAND COURT

Office
1 Grosvenor Crescent, Edinburgh, EH12 5ER.
Tel. 031-225-3595.

Chairman
Lord Elliott.

Members of Court
D. D. McDiarmid.
A. B. Campbell.
R. Macdonald.

Principal Clerk
Keith H. R. Graham.

THE SCOTTISH MILK MARKETING BOARD

Underwood Road, Paisley, PA3 1TJ.
Tel. 041-887-1234
Telex 779012
Fax 041-889-1225

Chairman
A. L. Howie.

Chief Executive
J. R. Laidlaw.

Secretary
J. M. S. Pirie.

Director of Regions and Farm Services
J. D. Hannah.

THE NORTH OF SCOTLAND MILK MARKETING BOARD

Claymore House, 29 Ardconnel Terrace, Inverness, IV2 3AF.
Tel. 0463-232611
Telex 75254

Chairman
H. Clark.

Managing Director
J. A. Anderson, BA (Hons).

Sales Manager
D. Watt.

Finance Director
I. Larg, FACCA.

Regional Officer
M. McLeod, BSc.

THE ABERDEEN AND DISTRICT MILK MARKETING BOARD

PO Box 117, Twin Spires, Bucksburn, Aberdeen, AB9 8AH.
Tel. 0224-696371

Chairman
I. Marr, Cultercullen, Udny, Ellon, AB4 0QP.

Chief Executive
T.R. Poynton.

Finance Controller
R. Stevens.

Regional Officer
A. Sim.

SCOTTISH PEAT AND LAND DEVELOPMENT ASSOCIATION

Crachin, Easter Howgate, Penicuik, Midlothian.
Tel. 031-445-2208 (evening) or 031-445-2147 (day)

Contact
Dr Brennan D. Soane—Secretary.

SCOTTISH QUALITY BEEF & LAMB ASSOCIATION LTD (SQBLA)

13th Avenue, Edinburgh Exhibition & Trade Centre, Ingliston, Edinburgh, EH28 8NB.
Tel. 031-333 5335
Fax. 031-333 2935
Telex. 72489

Contact
D.I. Brown—Director and Secretary

The Scotch Quality Beef and Lamb Association

SQBLA was created in 1974 to provide a marketing and promotional organisation for Scotch Quality Beef and Lamb. Formed by the National Farmers' Union of Scotland, the Institute of Auctioneers and Appraisers in Scotland, the Scottish Association of Meat Wholesalers and the Scottish Federation of Meat Traders Associations, SQBLA is governed by a Board of Management representing the founding organisations.

The Association carries out a wide range of promotional activities in Scotland, the rest of the U.K., the catering sector and the export market. The objective of the Association is simply to improve the image and sales of quality Scotch Beef and Lamb.

It achieves its objectives through promotional techniques which include store, independent butcher and hotel and restaurant promotions. Added to this is trade and public relations activities and increasingly important to SQBLA is the implementation of Quality Assurance and Product Development Schemes.

Participation at Trade Fairs and Exhibitions throughout the UK and Europe is an important part of SQBLA's activities. SQBLA works closely with such organisations as the MLC, Scottish Food Promotion, the Scottish Development agency and the Highlands and Islands Development Board to promote exposure of quality Scottish meat products to all the important markets in the world.

Operational Office: 13th Avenue, Edinburgh Exhibition & Trade Centre, Ingliston, Edinburgh EH28 8NB. Chairman:

John E. McNaughton, O.B.E., J.P., F.R.Ag.S. Deputy Chairman: Pat U. Lawson, O.B.E. Chief Executive: Ian Brown. U.K. promotions Manager: Victor Prow. Consumer & Education Manager: Margaret Johnston.

Tel. No. 031 333 5335   FAX No. 031 333 2935

SCOTTISH RECREATIONAL LAND ASSOCIATION

86 Comely Bank Avenue, Edinburgh, EH4 1HE
Tel. 031-332 0265

Contact
Ms P. H. Dewar

SCOTTISH RIGHTS OF WAY SOCIETY LTD

1 Lutton Place, Edinburgh, EH8 9PD.
Tel. 031-447-9242

Contact
Robert A. Dickson—Honorary Secretary.

SCOTTISH SOCIETY FOR THE PREVENTION OF CRUELTY TO ANIMALS (SSPCA)

19 Melville Street, Edinburgh, EH3 7PL.
Tel. 031-225-6418/9

Contact
Sir Cameron Rusby—Chief Executive.

SCOTTISH SOCIETY FOR THE PROTECTION OF WILD BIRDS

Foremount House, Kilbarchan, Renfrewshire, PA10 2EZ.
Tel. 05057-2419

Contact
Dr J. A. Gibson—Honorary Secretary and Treasurer.

SCOTTISH TOURIST BOARD HEADQUARTERS

23 Ravelston Terrace, Edinburgh, EH4 3EU.
Tel. 031-332-2433.

Contact
Tom Band—Chief Executive.

SCOTTISH TREE TRUST

30 Edgemont Street, Glasgow, G41 3EL.
Tel. 041-649-2462

Contact
Greer Hart—Founder/President.

SCOTTISH WOMEN'S RURAL INSTITUTES

42 Heriot Row, Edinburgh, EH3 6ES.
Tel. 031-225-1724

Contact
Eileen Nicol—General Secretary.

THE SMALLFARMERS' ASSOCIATION

14a Halswell House, Goathurst, Nr. Bridgwater, Somerset, TA5 2DS.
Tel. 0278-663032

TENANT FARMERS' ASSOCIATION

Hadwyn House, Field Road, Reading, Berks, RG1 6BJ.
Tel. 0734-391121

General Secretary
N.C. Forster.

UNITED FARMERS LTD

Claremont House, 19 Claremont Crescent, Edinburgh, EH7 4JW.
Tel. 031-557-2914

Managing Director
I.C. Weir.

UNITED KINGDOM AGRICULTURAL SUPPLY TRADE ASSOCIATION LTD

3 Whitehall Court, London, SW1A 2EQ.
Tel. 071-930-3611

Director General
J. W. Read.

VIRUS TESTED STEM CUTTING GROWERS' ASSOCIATION

8 Manor Place, Edinburgh, EH3 7DF.
Tel. 031-225-1466

Honorary Secretary
H. B. Edmond.

WILDLIFE TRUST-SCOTTISH OFFICE

Eastbank Farm, Caerlaverock, Dumfries, DG1 4RS.
Tel. 038777-200

Contact
J. B. Doherty—Refuge Manager

WOMEN'S FARMING UNION (in Scotland)

Knowes farm, Dunbar, East Lothian.

Contact
Hilary Cochran—Representative: Central Executive Council, Scotland

Headquarters
Crundalls, Matfield, Kent, TN12 7EA.
Tel. 089-272-2803

FORESTRY ORGANISATIONS

THE ASSOCIATION OF PROFESSIONAL FORESTERS
Brokerswood House, Brokerswood, Nr Westbury, Wiltshire.
Tel. Westbury 822238

Secretary
A. G. Phillips, Esq.

FORESTRY COMMISSION
231 Corstorphine Road, Edinburgh, EH12 7AT.
Tel. 031-334-0303

Contact
J. F. Lindsay—Principal Information Officer.

INSTITUTE OF CHARTERED FORESTERS (ICF)
22 Walker Street, Edinburgh, EH3 7HR.
Tel. 031-225-2705

Secretary
Margaret Dick

ROYAL SCOTTISH FORESTRY SOCIETY
11 Atholl Crescent, Edinburgh, EH3 8HE.
Tel. 031-229-1212

Secretary
William B. C. Walker

SCOTTISH SCHOOL OF FORESTRY
c/o Inverness College, 3 Longman Road, Inverness.
Tel. 0463-790431

TIMBER GROWERS UNITED KINGDOM
Agriculture House, Knightsbridge, London, SW1X 7NJ.
Tel. 071-235-2925

Contact
Claire Foottit—Publicity and Information Officer.

THE WOODLAND TRUST (SCOTLAND)
Scottish Office 1985
54 Manor Place, Edinburgh, EH3 7EH.
Tel. 031-225-3543

Manager
Pauline Hogg
Autumn Park, Grantham, Lincolnshire, NG31 6LL.
Tel. 0476-74297

DIVERSIFICATION

USEFUL NAMES AND ADDRESSES

The Association of British Sheep Dairying
Windy Knowe, Annan, Dumfriesshire, DG12 5LN.

The British Goat Society
Rougham, Bury St Edmunds, Suffolk, IP30 9LJ.

British Goat Society
Great Glen Foods, Old Ferry Road, North Ballachulish, Onich, Fort William, Inverness-shire, PH33 6RZ.

British Angora Goat Society
Brawliemuir Farm, Johnshaven, by Montrose, Angus, DD10 0HY.

Barony Agriculture College
(SCOTEC Certificate in Fish Farming), Parkgate, Dumfries.

The British Institute of Agricultural Consultants
Laurence Gould Consultants, 3 Rutland Square, Edinburgh, EH1 2AS.

Caravan Club Limited
East Grinstead House, East Grinstead, West Sussex, RH19 1VA.

The Fur Breeders' Association
Riverbank House, 67 Upper Thames Street, London, EC4V 3AB.

Free Range Egg Association
39 Maresfield Gardens, London, NW3.

Farm Shop & Pick Your Own Association
Hunger Lane, Muggington, Derbyshire, DE6 4PL.

The Guild of Conservation Food Producers
Bedford Silo, Mile Road, Bedford.

Highland Craftpoint
Beauly, Inverness-shire, IV4 7EH.

Institute of Agriculture
University of Stirling, Stirling.

Inverness Technical College
(Certificate in Aquaculture), Longman Road, Inverness.

The Macaulay Land Use Research Institute
Craigiebuckler, Aberdeen, AB9 2OJ.

The Organic Growers' Association
86 Colston Street, Bristol.

Organic Farmers & Growers Scotland
Glenside Farm, Plean, Stirling, FK7 8BA.

Scottish Salmon Growers' Association
Angus Mackenzie & Co., 1 View Place, Inverness.

Scottish Shellfish Growers' Association
Tigh Na Speir, Connel, Argyll.

Scottish Beekeeping Association
Richmond Villa, Dumfries, DG2 7JS.

Scottish Trekking and Riding Association
Tomnagairn Farm, Trochry, by Dunkeld.

Scottish Agritours
(Scottish Farmhouse Holidays), Drumtenant, Lady- bank, Fife, KY17 7UG.

Scottish Crop Research Institute
Invergowrie, Dundee, DD2 5DA.

Scottish Tourist Board
23 Ravelston Terrace, Edinburgh, EH4 3EU.

Scottish Angora Rabbits & British Commercial Rabbits Association
Ravenscraig, Roslin, Midlothian.

FAIR GAME

By Paul S. Blacklock

The Scots law on game and fishing is a patchwork. To establish the seasons during which sundry quarry can be taken, one must consult statutes passed in (at least) three centuries! The Scottish Landowners' Federation has, therefore, approached the Scottish Law Commission, again, to urge them to undertake consolidation of the legislation.

WHEN NOT TO SHOOT

1. Night shooting
The shooting of game at night is prohibited under the provisions of the Hares (Scotland) Act 1848, but under the Ground Game Act 1880, as amended by the Wildlife & Countryside Act 1981, occupiers of land, and those authorised by them, are allowed to shoot ground game only (hares and rabbits).

2. Christmas and Sundays
Although there is no statutory prohibition on the shooting of game on Sundays or Christmas Day it is not customary in Scotland to shoot on those days, and certainly not on Sunday mornings.

3. Close seasons
(a) The *Game (Scotland) Act 1772* provides for close seasons as follows:

Partridges	1 February to 1 September
Pheasants	1 February to 1 October
Muirfowl (Grouse) and Ptarmigan	10 December to 12 August
Heathfowl (blackgame)	10 December to 20 August

(b) The *Wildlife & Countryside Act 1981* provides for close seasons as follows:

Capercailzie	1 February to 30 September
Woodcock	1 February to 31 August
Common Snipe	1 February to 11 August
Coot	
Moorhen	1 February to 31 August
Plover, Golden	
Duck, Tufted	
Gadwall	
Goldeneye	
Goose, Canada	(a) In or over any area below high-water mark of ordinary spring tides:
Goose, Greylag	21 February to 31 August
Goose, Pink-footed	(b) In any other area:
Mallard	1 February to 31 August
Pintail	
Pochard	
Shoveler	
Teal	
Wigeon	

NB – The Whitefronted Goose is protected in Scotland; it enjoys a 'year-round close season'.

(c) The *Deer (Scotland) Act 1959* and the *Deer (Close) Seasons (Scotland) Order 1984* provide for close seasons as follows:

SPECIES	*MALE*	*FEMALE*
Red Deer Sika Deer and Red/Sika Hybrids	21 October to 30 June	16 February to 20 October
Fallow Deer	1 May to 31 July	16 February to 20 October
Roe Deer	21 October to 31 March	1 April to 20 October
Muntjac	No statutory close season	
Chinese Water Deer	No statutory close season	

ALL dates are inclusive.

WHEN NOT TO FISH

Salmon and Sea Trout
The annual close time for salmon and sea trout is 168 days, but the actual commencement and termination of this period may be varied in different salmon fishery districts. There is, however, an exception in favour of rod and line fishing and the close time for this method of fishing is shorter than 168 days. The rod and line close time varies in different districts and anglers are advised to find out in advance either locally, or from the Department of Agriculture and Fisheries for Scotland, what are the relevant dates for the waters they wish to fish.

Brown Trout
The annual close time for the common or brown trout is from 7 October to the following 14 March.

Rainbow Trout
No legislation regulates fishing for rainbow trout – there is, therefore, no close season.

TROUT FISHING RIGHTS

The only places that the public have the right to fish for trout is in the tidal reaches of a river or sea loch.

The following two important propositions have been laid down by the Court of Session (the highest civil court in Scotland):

(1) That there is no common right to fish for trout either in the public at large or in such members of the community as may have access to the water by virtue of a right of passage along the banks.

(2) That the continuous use and practice of fishing in such a stream for 40 years or more will not establish a right in the public or in the inhabitants of the neighbourhood, but must be ascribed to toleration by the proprietors (Grant v Henry (1894) 21 R.358).

Therefore any person who fishes for trout with rod and line and without the permission of the proprietor may be turned off without undue violence. Any person may also find himself liable civilly if he has caused damage and an interdict may be granted against them at their expense if there is reason to believe that they will continue to fish without permission.

GUN LAW

The ownership and use of firearms is a topic which generates much heat. Events in Hungerford incited public opinion which in turn aroused the Government to deal with the firearms issue (already slated for legislation) by bringing forward the Firearms (Amendment) Act 1988.
The Whitley Bay outrage prompted some to urge even tighter regulation but, given the hundreds of thousands with a legitimate need to possess firearms, it is difficult to see how legislation can prevent occasional incidents.

THE FIREARMS (AMENDMENT) ACT 1988

A. Section 5 weapons

Self-loading and pump-action centre-fire rifles are now to be regulated under section 5 of the 1968 Firearms Act and will therefore be banned, along with self-loading and pump-action smooth bore guns, other than those chambered for .22 rim-fire cartridges and meeting certain length standards for length of barrel, and overall length. Smooth bore revolvers are similarly prohibited, except for those chambered for 9mm rim-fire cartridges or muzzle loaded.

Any weapon which was ever classified under section 5, even if subsequently converted, will now revert to section 5. Rifles converted to shotguns will remain under section 2, provided the barrel length is over 24 inches.

B. Disposal of weapons rendered illegal

Deactivation verified by a Proof House will render the item no longer a firearm, legally speaking.
Provision was made for compensation for holders of banned self-loading and pump-action rifles, and burstfire weapons and rapid-fire short barrel shotguns.

C. (1) Shotguns

Self-loading and pump-action shotguns, if they are to continue under section 2 must be modified (as verified by a Proof House) to include as an integral part a non-detachable magazine with a capacity of two cartridges only. Otherwise they are now regulated under section 1 and require a firearms certificate.

(2) Shotgun certificates

These will have to list all the shotguns a person owns. The police may refuse a certificate if they are satisfied that the applicant lacks a good reason for possessing a shotgun, but they are not allowed to refuse one simply because the applicant intends neither to use nor lend the weapon. Sporting, competition or shooting vermin are to be regarded as good reasons.

(3) Security

Owners are required to keep their shotguns in a secure place. The publication 'Firearms Law: Guidance to the Police' gives some help on this subject. While it is largely left to police discretion, the guidelines advocate the fixing of the weapons to the fabric of the building. Otherwise, it is mostly a matter of commonsense.

(4) Transfers

Loans for no more than 72 hours do not require any formalities, provided always that the borrower has a shotgun certificate; otherwise both parties to a transfer require to notify, within 7 days, the chief of police responsible for issuing their certificates.

(5) Ammunition

The shotgun certificate must be produced in order to buy ammunition.

D. (1) Shotgun and Firearms Certificates

Four photographs will be required with applications, along with a statement from a responsible individual that he knows no reason why the applicant should not have a certificate. Individuals with both firearms and shotgun will probably have iheir expiry dates co-ordinated.

(2) Revocation of certificates

The chief of police is empowered to cancel firearms and shotgun certificates, in writing. There is provision for consequent surrender of weapons and ammunition, and for this to be immediate if circumstances warrant. The certificate holder has a right of appeal.

(3) Borrowing of rifles

On private premises anyone over the age of 17 can borrow a rifle provided it is used in the presence of the occupier or his servant, and that the individual supervising has a firearms certificate, and that the rifle is used in accordance with that certificate's conditions.

E. Visitors' permits

These certificates will be valid throughout Great Britain, for up to one year.

F. The future

Firearms rules are to supplement the primary legislation. As noted previously, a book has been issued 'Guidance to the Police'.

A 'Guidance to Gun Clubs' is to be issued. There are problems where people who do not hold a shotgun certificate, borrow a gun at a game fair, charity shoot, etc. An Exemption Certificate will normally be obtained from the police in advance of the event.

The Firearm Consultative Committee, consisting of a chairman and up to twelve others (including representatives of sport and competition), will for the next five years supervise the implementation of the legislation and report annually to Parliament.

G. Gun problems

Given the scale of the task, administratively, it would have been surprising if no problems had arisen. Complaints from owners include:–

—'requirement' that the gunowner prove permission to shoot at some specific location.

—demand that the guns be kept in a guncase.

—suggestions that the guest gun provision laid down in s.16 does not apply if the shoot is commercial, or if the person borrowing the gun is a tenant of the lender.

None of the positions appears justified by the terms of the legislation.

There is a widespread impression that the Legislation and Guidance code are subject to wide variations in police interpretation. The British Association of Shooting and Conservation is about to publish a survey of the application of firearms law; there is also a parallel study commissioned on behalf of the Chiefs of Police. Some of the problems will hopefully be ironed out by the Firearms Consultative Committee.

STATUTORY AUTHORITIES

ADAS
Great Westminster House, Horseferry Road, London, SW1.
Tel. 071-216-6311

Countryside Commission
John Dower House, Crescent Place, Cheltenham, Gloucestershire, GL50 3RA.
Tel. 02425-21381

Countryside Commission for Scotland
Battleby, Redgorton, Perth, PH1 3EW.
Tel. 0738-27921

DOE
Pollgate House, Houlton Street, Bristol, BS2 9DJ.
Tel. 0272-218811

Natural Environment Research Council
Polaris House, North Star Avenue, Swindon, Wiltshire, SN2 1EU.
Tel. 0793-401 01

Nature Conservancy Council
Northminster House, Peterborough, PE1 1UA.
Tel. 0733-40345

Red Deer Commission
Knowsley, 82 Fairfield Road, Inverness, IV3 5LH.
Tel. 04632-31751

Sports Council
16 Upper Woburn Place, London, WC1H 0QP.
Tel. 071-388-1277

VOLUNTARY ASSOCIATIONS

Anglers' Cooperative Association
Midland Bank Chambers, Westgate, Grantham, NG31 6LE.
Tel. 0476-61008

Association of Masters of Harriers and Beagles
Horn Park, Beaminster, Dorset, DT8 3HB.
Tel. 0308-862212

Atlantic Salmon Trust
Moulin, Pitlochry, Perthshire, PH16 5JQ.
Tel. 0796-3439

British Association for Shooting and Conservation
Marford Mill, Chester Road, Rossett, Wrexham, Clwyd, LL12 0HL.
Tel. 0244-570881

British Deer Society
Church Farm, Lower Basildon, Reading, Berkshire, RG8 9NH.
Tel. 07357-4094

British Falconers' Club
D. Stoodley, Sand Cottage, Milton Road, Stadhampton, Oxon, OX9 7UD.

British Field Sports Society Scotland
Glenmore Lodge, Moffat, Dumfriesshire.
Tel. 0683-20571
Secretary, Lt-Colonel D. D. Burns.

British Field Sports Society
59 Kennington Road, London, SE1 7PZ.
Tel. 071-928-4742

British Horse Society
British Equestrian Centre, Stoneleigh, Kenilworth, Warks, CV8 2LR.
Tel. 0203-52241

British Shooting Sports Council
Secretary, Pentridge, Salisbury, Wiltshire.
Tel. 0722-55370

British Trust for Ornithology
Beech Grose, Station Road, Tring, Herts, HP23 5NR.
Tel. 044-282-3461

The British Waterfowl Association
6 Caldicott Close, Over Winsford, Cheshire, CW7 1LW.
Tel. 0606-594150

Clay Pigeon Shooting Association
107 Epping New Road, Buckhurst Hill, Essex, IG9 5TQ.
Tel. 081-505-6221

Council for Country Sports
Welbeck House, High Street, Guildford, Surrey, GU1 3JF.
Tel. 0483-33448

Country Gentlemen's Association
Icknield Way West, Letchworth, Hertfordshire, SG6 4AP.
Tel. 0462-682377

Country Landowners' Association
16 Belgrave Square, London, SW1X 8PQ.
Tel. 071-235-0511

CLA Game Fair
Director, R. Rees-Webbe, The Game Fair, Claremont House, Claremont Bank, Shrewsbury, SY1 1RJ.
Tel. 0743-242127

FACE (UK)
Marford Mill, Chester Road, Rossett, Clwyd, LL12 0HL.
Tel. 0244-570881

Farming & Wildlife Advisory Group
RASE, National Agricultural Centre, Kenilworth, Warwickshire.
Tel. 0203-56161

Field and Country Sports Society of Ireland
M. C. A. Jackson, Ferndale, Kilpedder, Greystones, Co. Wicklow.

Tel. Greystones 874317

Flyfishers' Club
24a Old Burlington Street, London, W1.
Tel. 071-734-9229

The Fly Dressers' Guild
The Weather House, Croxley Hall Woods, Nr. Rickmansworth, Herts.
Tel. 0923-778544

The Game Conservancy
Fordingbridge, Hants, SP6 1EF.
Head of Advisory Services Scotland, I. H. L. McCall.
Tel. 082-85-543

Game Farmers' Association
S. Jervis-Read, CBE MC, The Cottage, Little Chart, Ashford, Kent.
Tel. 023-384-610

Gun Trade Association Limited
N. Brown, Fairbourne Cottage, Bunny Lane, Timsbury, Nr. Romsey, Hampshire, SO5 0PG.
Tel. 0794-68443

Kennel Club
1 Clarges Street, London, W1.
Tel. 071-493-6651

Masters of Foxhounds Association
Parsloes Cottage, Bagendon, Cirencester, Gloucestershire.
Tel. 028-583-470

National Farmers' Union
Agriculture House, Knightsbridge, London, SW1.
Tel. 071-235-5077

National Federation of Anglers
Halliday House, 2 Wilson Street, Derby, DE1 1PG.
Tel. 0332-362000

National Game Dealers' Association
1 Belgrove, Tunbridge Wells, Kent, TN1 1YW.
Tel. 0892-41412

Nature Conservancy Council
North Minster House, Peterborough, PE1 1UA.
Tel. 0733-40345

Royal Agricultural Society of England
National Agricultural Centre, Kenilworth, Warwickshire.
Tel. 0203-56161

Royal Society for Nature Conservation
The Green, Nettleham, Lincolnshire, LN2 2NR.
Tel. 0522-752326

Royal Society for the Protection of Birds
The Lodge, Sandy, Bedfordshire, SG19 2DL.
Tel. 0767-80551

Salmon & Trout Association
Fishmongers' Hall, London, EC4.
Tel. 071-626-3531

The Wildfowl Trust
Slimbridge, Gloucestershire, GL2 7BT.
Tel. 0453-89333

World Pheasant Association
PO Box 5, Child Beale Wildlife Trust, Lower Basildon, Reading, Berkshire, RG8 9PF.
Tel. 049-162271

World Wide Fund for Nature
Panda House, Weyside Park, Godalming, Surrey, GU7 1XR.
Tel. 0483-426444

Royal Society for the Protection of Birds
The Lodge, Sandy, Bedfordshire, SG19 2DL.
Tel. 0767-80551

Salmon & Trout Association
Fishmongers' Hall, London, EC4.
Tel. 071-626-3531

The Wildfowl Trust
Slimbridge, Gloucestershire, GL2 7BT.
Tel. 0453-89333

World Pheasant Association
PO Box 5, Child Beale Wildlife Trust, Lower Basildon, Reading, Berkshire, RG8 9PF.
Tel. 049-162271

World Wide Fund for Nature
Panda House, Weyside Park, Godalming, Surrey, GU7 1XR.
Tel. 0483-426444

NATIONAL FOOD TRADE

USEFUL ADDRESSES

Association of British Abattoir Owners
8 Hayne Street, London, EC1A 9HH.
Tel. 071-608-8675

Association of Meat Inspectors
10 Shaftsbury Avenue, New Barnet, Herts, EN5 5JA.
Tel. 081-440-8712

Bacon & Meat Manufacturers' Association
18-19 Cornwall Terrace, London, NW1 4QP.
Tel. 071-935-7980

British Association of Canned & Preserved Food Importers & Distributors
1 London Bridge, London, SE1.
Tel. 071-403-0141

British Bacon Bureau
26 Fitzroy Square, London, W1P 6BT.
Tel. 071-388-7421

British Duck Advisory Bureau
Thames View House, 6 St Peter's Road, Twickenham, Middlesex, PW1 1OX.
Tel. 081-892-2720

British Egg Association
High Holborn House, 52-54 High Holborn, London, WC1V 6SX.
Tel. 071-242-4683

British Food Manufacturing Industries Research Association
Randalls Road, Leatherhead, Surrey, KT22 7RY.
Tel. Leatherhead 76761

British Frozen Food Federation
Honeypot Lane, Colsterworth, Grantham, Lincs, NG33 6LY.
Tel. Corby Glen 414

British Multiple Retailers' Association
Commonwealth House, 1-19 New Oxford Street, London, WC1A 1PA.
Tel. 071-404-0955

The British Poultry Federation
High Holborn House, 52-54 High Holborn, London, WC1V 6SX.
Tel. 071-242-4683

British Poultry Information Service
100 Wigmore Street, London, W1H 9DR.
Tel. 071-486-1266

British Refrigeration & Air Conditioning Association
3 Phoenix House, Phoenix Way, Heston, Middx, TW5 9ND.
Tel. 081-897-3243

British Sausage Bureau
26 Fitzroy Square, London, W1P 6BT.
Tel. 071-388-7421

British Standards Institution
2 Park Street, London, W1A 2BS.
Tel. 071-629-9000

Central Office of Information
Hercules Road, London, SE1 7DU.
Tel. 071-928-2345

Commercial Rabbit Association
Tyning House, Shurdington, Cheltenham, Glos, GL51 5XF.
Tel. 0242-862387

Commission of the European Communities
Information Office, 20 Kensington Palace Gardens, London, W8 4QG.
Tel. 071-727-8090

Commonwealth Secretariat
Marlborough House, London, SW1Y 5HX.
Tel. 071-839-3411

Consumers' Association
14 Buckingham Street, London, WC2N 6DS.
Tel. 071-839 -1222

Danish Agricultural Producers
2-3 Conduit Street, London, W1R 0AT.
Tel. 071-499-7040

Danish Bacon Export Factories' Association
(Ess-Food (UK) Ltd), 364-366 Kensington High Street, London, W14 8NT.
Tel. 071-603-4577

Delicatessen & Fine Foods Association
3 Fairfield Avenue, Staines, Middx.
Tel. 0784-61339

Duck Producers' Association
High Holborn House, 52-54 High Holborn, London, WC1V 6SX.
Tel. 071-242-4683

Dutch Meat Promotion Bureau
PO Box 197, London, SE1 9SZ.
Tel. 071-387-9311

European Cold Storage Association (AEEF)
Avenue de Broquebille 272, Bte 4, B-1200 Brussels, Belgium.
Tel. (02) 771-3635
Telex 26458

European Parliament (Information Office)
2 Queen Anne's Gate, London, SW1H 9AA.
Tel. 071-222-0411

Exports Credits Guarantee Department
Aldermanbury House, Aldermanbury Square, London, EC2P 2EL.
Tel. 071-606-6699

Farmars' Union of Wales
Llys Amaeth, Queen's Square, Aberystwyth.
Tel. Aberystwyth 612755

Federation of Fresh Meat Wholesalers
8 Hayne Street, London, EC1A 9HH.
Tel. 071-606-8675

Food & Drink Industries Council
25 Victoria Street, London, SW1.
Tel. 071-222-1533

Food, Drink & Tobacco Industries Training Board
Barton House, Barton Street, Gloucester, GL1 1QQ.
Tel. 0452-28621

Food From Britain
c/o Central Council for Agricultural & Horticultural Co-operation, 301-344 Market Towers, New Covent Garden Market, London.
Tel. 071-720-2144

Food Manufacturers' Federation
6 Catherine Street, London, WC2B 5JJ.
Tel. 071-836-1460

Freight Transport Association Ltd
Head Office, Hermes House, St John's Wood Road, Tunbridge Wells, Kent, TN4 9UZ.
Tel. 0892-26171

Health & Safety Executive
39 Baddow Road, Chelmsford, Essex, CM2 0HL.
Tel. 0245-84661

Heating & Ventilating Contractors' Association
(Refrigeration and Unit Air Conditioning Group), ESCA House, 34 Palace Court, Bayswater, London, W2 4JG.
Tel. 071-229-2488

Home Grown Cereals Authority
Hamlyn House, Highgate Hill, London, N19 5PR.
Tel. 071-263-3391
Telex 27615

HM Customs & Excise
King's Beam House, Mark Lane, London, EC3R 7HE.
Tel. 071-626-1515

The Hide & Allied Trades Improvements Society
18 High Street, Bridgwater, Somerset, TA6 3BJ.
Tel. 0278-55026

International Association of Fish Meal Manufacturers
Hoval House, Mutton Lane, Potters Bar, Hertfordshire, EN6 3AR.
Tel. 0707-42343

International Association of Refrigerated Warehouses
7315 Wisconsin Avenue, Bethesda, MD 20814, USA.

International Institute of Refrigeration
177 Boulevard Malesherbes, 75017 Paris, France.
Tel. 227-32035

International Meat Trade Association
8 Hayne Street, London, EC1A 9HH.
Tel. 071-606-8675

Intervention Board for Agricultural Produce
PO Box 69, Fountain House, 2 West Mall, Reading, Berks, RG1 7QW.
Tel. 0734-583626

Institute of Meat
Boundary House, 91-93 Charterhouse Street, London, EC1M 6HR.
Tel. 071-253-2971

The Institute of Refrigeration
76 Mill Lane, Carshalton, Surrey, SM5 2JR.
Tel. 081-647-7033

Institute of Shops, Health & Safety Acts Administration
23 Grand Avenue, Muswell Hill, London, N10.
Tel. 071-883-6803

Institute of Trading Standards Administration
Estate House, 319d London Road, Hadleigh, Benfleet, Essex.
Tel. Southend 558179

Institution of Environmental Health Officers
Chadwick House, Rushworth Street, London, SE1 0RB.
Tel. 071-928-6006

Irish Livestock & Meat Board
26-28 Bedford Row, London, WC1R 4HE.
Tel. 071-405-1772

Joint Consultative Council for the Meat Trade
c/o 1 Belgrove, Tunbridge Wells, Kent, TN1 1YW.
Tel. 0892-44046/7

Joint Industrial Council for the Retail Meat Trade: Employers' Side
c/o 1 Belgrove, Tunbridge Wells, Kent, TN1 1YW.
Tel. 0892-44046/7

Livestock Traders' Association of Great Britain Ltd
Regent House, Clinton Avenue, Nottingham, NG5 1AZ.
Tel. 0602-608177

Meat Industry Training Organisation
c/o Institute of Meat, Boundary House, 91-93 Charterhouse Street, London, EC1M 6HR.
Tel. 071-253-2971

Meat Promotion Executive
5 St John's Square, London, EC1M 4DE.
Tel. 071-252-2021

Most Research Institute
Agricultural Research Council, Langford, Bristol, Avon. BS18 7DY.
Tel. Churchill 661

Ministry of Agriculture, Fisheries & Food (Meat Group)
Whitehall Place, London, SW1.
Tel. 071-233-3000

National Association of British Market Authorities
54 St Paul's Hill Road, Hyde, Cheshire, SK14 2SW.

National Association of Tripedressers
Elvian House 18-20 St Andrew Street, London, EC4 3AE.
Tel. 071-353-3055

National Chamber of Trade
Enterprise House, Henley-on-Thames, Oxon, RG9 1TU.
Tel. 049-12-6161

National Cold Storage Federation
Tavistock House North, Tavistock Square, London, WC1H 9HZ.
Tel. 071-388-7766

The National Farmers' Union
Agriculture House, Knightsbridge, London, SW1X 7NG.
Tel. 071-235-5077

National Federation of Hide & Skin Markets
66 High Street, Great Missenden, Bucks.
Tel. 02406-2644

National Federation of Meat Traders
1 Belgrove, Tunbridge Wells, Kent, TN1 1YW.
Tel. 0892-44047

National Federation of Wholesale Poultry Merchants
1 Belgrove, Tunbridge Wells, Kent, TN1 1YW.
Tel. 0892-44046/7

National Game Dealers' Association
1 Belgrove, Tunbridge Wells, Kent, TN1 1YW.
Tel. 0892-44046/7

National Institute for Research in Dairying
Shinfield, Reading, Berks, RG2 9AT.
Tel. Reading 883103

National Pig Breeders' Association
7 Rickmansworth Road, Watford, Herts, WD1 7HE.
Tel. 0923-34377

National Sausage Casings Association
21 Lansdowne Avenue, Orpington, Kent, BR6 8JT.
Tel. Farnborough (Kent) 54907

New Zealand Lamb Information Bureau
The Cloisters, 11 Salem Road, London, W2 4BU.
Tel. 071-221-0990

New Zealand Meat Producers' Board
53 Chancery Lane, London WC1.
Tel. 071-405-7904

The Retail Consortium
19 Buckingham Gate, London, SW1E 6LB.
Tel. 071-834-9526

Road Haulage Association
22 Upper Woburn Place, London, WC1H 0ES.
Tel. 071-387-9711

The Royal Smithfield Club
Brierley House, Summer Lane, Combe Down, Bath, BA2 5LE.
Tel. 0225-837904

Scottish Federation of Meat Traders' Associations
Craigie House, Craigie Knowes Road, Perth, PH2 0DQ.
Tel. 0738 37785

Skin, Hide & Leather Traders' Association
69 Cannon Street, London, EC4N 5AB.
Tel. 071-248-4444

Smithfield Market Tenants' Association
327a Central Markets, London, EC1.
Tel. 071-248-3151

UK Association of Frozen Food Producers
1 Green Street, Grosvenor Square, London, W1Y 3RG.
Tel. 071-629-0655

US Meat Exporters' Federation
47 Upper Grosvenor Street, London, W1.
Tel. 071-499-8252

Worshipful Company of Butchers
Butchers' Hall, 87 Bartholomew Close, London, EC1A 7ER
Tel. 071-606-4106

BRITISH SOCIETY OF ANIMAL PRODUCTION

OFFICERS
President
Dr Maurice Bichard, Pig Improvement Company Ltd, Fyfield Wick, Abingdon, Oxon, OX13 5NA.
Tel. 0865-820654

Senior Vice-President
Dr Jim O'Grady, IAWS Group plc, 1 51 Thomas Street, Dublin, 8.
Tel. 0001-71-7131

Honorary Secretary
Dr Graham Gunn, BSAP, PO Box 3, Penicuik, Midlothian, EH26 0RZ.
Tel. 031-445-4508

Press Officer
Dr Mike Wilkinson, Chalcombe Publications, Honey Lane, Hurley, Maidenhead, Berks, SL6 5LR.
Tel. 062-882-6868

BSAP Office
PO Box 3, Penicuik, Midlothian, EH26 0RZ.
Tel. 031-445-4508

AGRICULTURAL AND FOOD RESEARCH

AFRC CENTRAL OFFICE
Wiltshire Court, Farnsby Street, Swindon, SN1 5AT.
Tel. 0793-514242
Fax. 0793-514788

Director
Dr B. G. Jamieson, PhD.

AFRC INSTITUTE FOR ANIMAL HEALTH

AFRC & MRC Neuropathogenesis Unit
Ogston Building, West Mains Road, Edinburgh, EH9 3JF.
Tel. 031-667-5204/5
Director
J. Hope, PhD.

AFRC INSTITUTE OF ANIMAL PHYSIOLOGY & GENETICS RESEARCH

Edinburgh Research Station
Roslin, Midlothian, EH25 9PS.
Tel. 031-440-2726
Fax. 031-440-0434

Head of Station
Dr G. Bulfield.

AFRC INSTITUTE FOR GRASSLAND AND ANIMAL PRODUCTION

Director of Research
Professor J. L. Stoddart, DSc, FIBiol. (at WPSB)

PLANT SCIENCE DIVISION
Welsh Plant Breeding Station
Plas Gogerddan, Aberystwyth, SY23 3EB.
Tel. 0970-828255
Fax. 0970-828357

Director
Professor D. Wilson.

GRASSLAND & RUMINANT DIVISION
Hurley Research Station
Maidenhead, Berkshire, SL6 5LR.
Tel. 062-882-3631
Fax. 062-882-3630

Head of Division
R. J. Wilkins, PhD.

North Wykeham Research Station
Okehampton, Devon, EX20 2SB.
Tel. 083-782-558
Fax. 083-782-139

PIG & POULTRY DIVISION
Roslin Research Station (Poultry Dept)
Roslin, Midlothian, EH25 9PS.
Tel. 031-440-2726
Fax. 031-440-0434

Shinfield Research Station (Pig Dept)
Church Lane, Shinfield, Reading, Berkshire, RG2 9AQ.
Tel. 0734-883-103
Fax. 0734-884-183

SCOTTISH AGRICULTURAL RESEARCH INSTITUTES

Grant-aided by the Department of Agriculture & Fisheries for Scotland

Hannah Research Institute
Ayr, Scotland, KA6 5HL.
Tel. 0292-76013/7
Fax. 0292-671052
Director
Professor M. Peaker, PhD, FIBiol, FRSE.
Secretary
Mrs M. W. Scott.

Macaulay Land Use Research Institute
Craigiebuckler, Aberdeen, AB9 2QJ.
Tel. 0224-318611
Fax. 0224-311556
Director
Professor T. J. Maxwell, BSc, PhD.
Secretary
Miss E. A. Piggott.

Macaulay Land Use Research Institute
Pentlandfield, Roslin, Midlothian, EH25 9RF.
Tel. 031-445-3401
Fax. 031-445-4035

Moredun Research Institute
408 Gilmerton Road, Edinburgh, EH17 7JH.
Tel. 031-664-3262
Director
I. D. Aitken, PhD, BVBS, MRCVS.

Rowett Research Institute
Greenburn Road, Bucksburn, Aberdeen, AB2 9SB.
Tel. 0224-712751
Director
Professor W. P. T. James, MD, DSc, FRCP, FRCP(E).

Scottish Crop Research Institute
Invergowrie, Dundee, DD2 5DA.
Tel. 0382-562731
Director
Professor J. Hillman, FIBiol, FLS, FRSE.

Scottish Agricultural Statistics Service
University of Edinburgh, James Clerk Maxwell Building, The King's Buildings, Mayfield Road, Edinburgh, EH9 3JZ.
Tel. 031-667-1081
Director
R. A. Kempton, DPhil.

BRITISH VETERINARY ASSOCIATION DIVISIONS (SCOTLAND) 1989

NORTH OF SCOTLAND DIVISION
President
Ian Murray, 35 Dunecht Road, Westhill, Aberdeen, AB3 6RH

Secretary
A. Simmons, DAFS, Animal Health Office, Government Buildings, Guild Street, Aberdeen.
Tel. 0224-574567

WEST OF SCOTLAND DIVISION
President
Ms Sue Henderson, PDSA, 1 Shamrock Street, Glasgow.
Tel. 041-332-6944

Secretary
Mrs M. B. M. Jackson, 2 Cotton Street, Balfron by Glasgow.
Tel. Balfron 40153

SCOTTISH METROPOLITAN DIVISION
President
Mr D. Ashworth, Veterinary Centre, Union Terrace, Crieff, Perthshire.
Tel. 0764-2086

Secretary
Dr E. Milne, Royal (Dick) School of Veterinary Studies, Department of Veterinary Clinical Studies, Veterinary Field Station, Easter Bush, Roslin, Midlothian, EH25 9RG.
Tel. 031-445-2001

DUMFRIES & GALLOWAY DIVISION
President
Mr A. W. Miller, Union Villa, Livingstone Place, Lockerbie, Dumfries, DG11 2AU.

Secretary
Mr R. Muir, Glen Brassnock, Corstorphine Road, Thornhill, Dumfries.

AYRSHIRE DIVISION
President
Mr D. Crawford, 58 Fort Street, Ayr.
Tel. Ayr 266102

Secretary
Mr D. Gray, Scottish Agricultural Colleges, Veterinary Investigation Centre, Auchincruive, KA6 5AE.
Tel. 0292-520331

SCOTTISH BRANCH
President
Mr W. J. Reilly, Communicable Diseases (Scotland) Unit, Ruchill Hospital, Glasgow, G20 9NB.
Tel. 041-946-7120, Ext 249

Secretary
Mr A. Greig, Veterinary Investigation Centre, Bush Estate, Penicuik, EH26 0QE.
Tel. 031-445-4811

MACHINERY

SCOTTISH AGRICULTURAL MACHINERY REPRESENTATIVES ASSOCIATION

Chairman
S. Bull, 9 Mapledean Road, Perth, PH2 6NY.
Tel. 0738-52436

Vice-Chairman
C. M. Singer, 33 Old Kirk Road, Dunfermline, Fife, KY12 7SQ.
Tel. 0383-725811

Secretary/Treasurer
R. Duncan, 10 Ashgrove, Scone, Perth.
Tel. 0738-51554

Membership Secretary
C. D. Rainbow, Timpendean Cottage, No. 8, Jedburgh, Roxburghshire, TD8 6SS.
Tel. 08353-326

SCOTTISH CENTRE OF AGRICULTURAL ENGINEERING

Bush Estate, Penicuik, Midlothian, EH26 0PH
Tel. 031-445-2147
Fax 031-445-2778

SCOTTISH CONSUMER COUNCIL

4 Somerset Place, Glasgow, G3.
Tel. 041-332-3377

SCOTTISH COOPERATIVE MILK TRADE ASSOCIATION

Mr C. Faulkiner, CWS Ltd, Milk Department, 130 Morrison Street, Glasgow, G5 8LP.
Tel. 041-429-2100

SCOTTISH DAIRY TRADE FEDERATION

A. W. Wiseman, Robert Wiseman & Sons Ltd, 159 Glasgow Road, East Kilbride, G74 4PA.
Tel. 035-52-44261

W. R. Hinchliffe, Esq, Hamilton's Dairies Ltd, Cairn Place, Nerston Industrial Estate, East Kilbride, G74 4NO.
Tel. 035-52-47777

SCOTTISH SEED POTATO DEVELOPMENT COUNCIL

Chief Executive
John Bethell, 2 The Sands, Haddington, East Lothian, EH41 3EY.
Tel. 062-082-4133
Fax. 062-082-4135

Chairman
James Stobo, O.B.E., Fishwick, Berwick.

Vice-Chairman
Guthrie Fenton, PBI (Fenton) Ltd, Dunkeld Road, Perth.

BREED SOCIETIES

CATTLE

Aberdeen Angus Cattle Society
R. Anderson, Pedigree House, 6 King's Place, Perth.
Tel. 0738-22477

Ayrshire Cattle Society
Stuart Thomson, PO Box 8, 1 Racecourse Road, Ayr.
Tel. 0292-267123

Belted Galloway Cattle Society
J. M. C. Rutherford, Rutherford Lodge, Kelso, Roxburghshire, TD5 8NW.
Tel. 083-52-3757

British Holstein Society
Chief Executive, K. J. Ellis, Foley House, 28 Worcester Road, Malvern, Worcs, WR14 4QW.

British Charolais Cattle Society Ltd
The Secretary, 19 Coventry Road, Cubbington, Leamington Spa, Warwickshire, CV32 7JN.

British Gelbvieh Cattle Society
F. C. Culley, 17 Fisher Street, Carlisle, CA3 8RF.

British Limousin Cattle Society
Peter Reynolds, Avenue Q, National Agricultural Centre, Stoneleigh, Kenilworth, Warwickshire, CV8 2RA.

British Romagnola Cattle Society Ltd
Miss Audrey M. Fenton, 26 York Place, Perth.
Tel. 0738-23780/22820

British Simmental Cattle Society
D. S. Gaunt, National Agricultural Centre, Kenilworth, Warwickshire, CV8 2LR.

Chianina Cattle Breed Society
Allan Errey, 44 Wallshead Way, Church Aston, Newport, Shropshire, TF10 9JF.
Tel. 0952-812970

Devon Cattle Breeders' Society
Secretary, D. B. J. Thompson, LVO, 24 Courtenay Park, Newton Abbot, Devon, TQ12 2HB.
Tel. 0626-67661

Dexter Cattle Society
Mr D. Key, Whitehouse Farm, No Mans Heath, Tamworth, Staffs, B79 0NX.
Tel. 0827-830432

English Guernsey Cattle Society
The Administrator, The Bury Farm, Pednor Road, Chesham, Bucks, HP5 2LA.

Galloway Cattle Society
Chris Graves, 15 New Market Street, Castle Douglas, DG7 1HY.

Gloucester Cattle Society
Secretary, Miss E. L. Henson, MA, MSc, Bemborough Farm Office, Guiting Power, Cheltenham, Glos.
Tel. 04515-307 (9am-5pm only)

Hereford Herd Book Society
D. E. Prothero, Hereford House, 3 Offa Street, Hereford, HR1 2LL.
Tel. 0432-272057

The Highland Cattle Society
A. H. G. Wilson, Blackchub, Keir, Thornhill, Dumfries, DG3 4DH.
Tel. 0848-30438

Holstein Friesian Cattle Society of Great Britain and Ireland
Mr D. G. Spring, Scotsbridge House, Rickmansworth, Herts. WD3 3BB.

Jersey Cattle Society of the United Kingdom
B. J. LeBrun, Jersey House, 154 Castle Hill, Reading, Berkshire, RG1 7RP.

Lincoln Red Cattle Society
J. P. Skehel, Lincolnshire Showground, Grange-de-Lings, Lincoln, LN2 2NA.
Tel. 0522-22900

The Longhorn Cattle Society
Secretary, Miss E. L. Henson, MA, MSc, Bemborough Farm Office, Guiting Power, Cheltenham, Glos.
Tel. 04515-307 (9am-5pm only)

The Luing Cattle Society Ltd
Ellangowan, Gilmerton, Crieff, Perthshire, PH7 3LZ.
Tel. 0764-3497

Maine-Anjou Cattle Society of the United Kingdom Ltd
G. M. Bradley, The Old Farm House, Brook End, Little Dunmow, Dunmow, Essex, CM6 3AA.
Tel. Stebbing 037-186-234

Marchigiana Cattle Breed Society Ltd
G. M. Bradley, The Old Farm House, Brook End, Little Dunmow, Essex, CM6 3AA.
Tel. Stebbing 037-186-234

Red Poll Cattle Society
P. Ryder-Davies, 6 Church Street, Woodbridge, Suffolk.
Tel. Wickham Market 746534

Shorthorn Society of the United Kingdom of Great Britain and Ireland
J. H. Wood Roberts, 4th Street, National Agricultural Centre, Stoneleigh Park, Kenilworth, Warwickshire, CV8 2LG.
Tel. 0203-696549

South Devon Herd Book Society
J. H. Pappin, 24 Courtenay Park, Newton Abbot, Devon, TQ12 2HB.
Tel. 0626-67661/67662

Sussex Cattle Society
Miss Sue Kennedy, Station Road, Robertsbridge, East Sussex, TN32 5DG.

Welsh Black Cattle Society
D. E. Davies, 13 Bangor Street, Caernarvon.

Whitebred Shorthorn Association Ltd
Mrs R. Mitchinson, Oak Hill, Kirkcambeck, Brampton, Cumbria, CA8 2BL.
Tel. 069-78-350

SHEEP

Badger Faced Welsh Mountain Sheep Society
Miss H. Barnes, Darven Foch, Pontshaen, Llandyssul, Dyfed, SA44 4UY.
Tel. 054555-238/376

Beulah Speckled-Face
D. J. Jones, Campbell & Edwards, 6 Market Street, Builth Wells, Powys.
Tel. 0982-553614

Blackface Sheep Breeders' Association
Miss Audrey Fenton, 26 York Place, Perth.
Tel. 0738-23780/22820

Black Welsh Mountain Sheep Breeders' Association
D. V. Child, MBE, Brierley House, Summer Lane, Combe Down, Bath, BA2 5LE.
Tel. 0225-837904

Bluefaced Leicester Sheep Breeders' Association
Miss Fiona Sloan, Kirkbeck, Clarencefield, Dumfries.

Border Leicester Sheep Breeders
Colin Douglas, 7 Laichpark Road, Edinburgh, EH14 1UL.
Tel. 031-444-1408

The British Charollais Sheep Society Ltd
Mrs C. Barber, Youngman's Road, Wymondham, Norfolk, NR18 9PJ.
Tel. 0953-603-335

The British Oldenburg Sheep Society Ltd
V. V. Pope, Nackington Farms, Canterbury, Kent, CT4 7AD.
Tel. 0227-463219

British Texel Sheep Society Ltd
Executive Officer, Jean Barber, National Agricultural Centre, Stoneleigh, Kenilworth, Warwickshire, CV8 2LG.
Tel. 0203-696629

Cambridge Sheep Society
Alun Davies, Pharm House, Neston Road, Willaston, South Wirral, L64 2TF.

Cheviot Sheep Society
J. F. Hamilton, 34 Ednam Street, Annan, DS12 6EF.
Tel. 04612-5349

Clun Forest Sheep Breeders' Society Ltd
The Secretary, David Uffolk, 25 Corve Street, Ludlow, Shropshire.
Tel. 0584-2251

Colbred Sheep Society Ltd
A. O. Colburn, Crickley Barrow, Northleach, Chel-tenham, Glos.
Tel. 0451-60330

Cotswold Sheep Society
Miss E. L. Henson, MA, MSc, Bemborough Farm Office, Guiting Power, Cheltenham, Glos.
Tel. 04515-307 (9am-5pm only)

Dalesbred Sheep Breeders' Association
J. Whitaker, Gib Hey Cottage, Chipping, Nr Preston, Lancs.
Tel. 099-56-570

Dartmoor Sheep Breeders' Association
Mrs Hanney, 3a Fore Street, South Brent, Devon.
Tel. 0364-73657

Derbyshire Gritstone Sheep Breeders' Society
E. Halsall, 528 Red Lees Road, Cliviger, Nr Burnley, Lancs, BB10 4TD.
Tel. 0282-27302

Devon Closewool Sheep Breeders' Society
Albert Beer, BSc, MS, DipAgric, FPH, Barn Lane Farm, Stoke Rivers, Barnstaple, North Devon, EX32 7LD.
Tel. Brayford 495

Devon and Cornwall Longwool Flockbook Association
A. V. Phillips, Sunridge, Bedford, Winkleigh, North Devon.
Tel. 08053-223

Dorset Down Sheep Breeders' Association
D. V. Child, MBE, Brierley House, Summer Lane, Combe Down, Bath, BA2 5LE.
Tel. 0225-837-904

Dorset Horn & Poll Dorset Sheep Breeders' Association
A. C. Robinson, B.Sc., FRICS, Westgate House, 45 High West Street, Dorchester, Dorset.
Tel. 0305-62126

Exmoor Horn Sheep Breeders' Society
Mrs H. Leeves, Pickedstones, Simonsbath, Somerset.
Tel. 83253

Hampshire Down Sheep Breeders' Association
Ivy Cottage, Netheravon, Salisbury, Wilts.
Tel. 0980-70557

Herdwick Sheep Breeders' Association
W. Bland, 1 Beckbank Cottages, Thwaites, Millom, Cumbria.
Tel. 065-76-677

Jacob Sheep Society
Mrs J. Earll, The Pines, 242 Ringwood Road, St Leonards, Ringwood, Hants, BH24 2SB.
Tel. Ferndown 0202-894319

Kerry Flock Book Society
Mrs G. Pugh, 41 Oak Drive, Oswestry, Shropshire, SY11 2RX.

Llanwenog Sheep Society
Miss J. King, Waun-Las, Taliains, Llandeilo, Dyfed. SA19 7DF.
Tel. 0558 685576

Lleyn Sheep Society
Secretary, Gwenda Roberts, Gwyndy, Bryncroes, Sarn, Pwllheli, Gwynedd.
Tel. 0758-83-357

Lonk Sheep Breeders' Association
Mrs M. Heys, Jack Hey Lane Farm, Cliviger, Nr Burnley, Lancs.
Tel. 0282-22709

Masham Sheep Breeders' Association
Secretary, Mrs Bainbridge, Gatehouse Cottage, Ellerton Abbey, Richmond, North Yorkshire, DN1 6AN.

North Country Cheviot Sheep Society
E. H. McDonald, Tigh Na Machair, Davochfin, Dornoch, Sutherland, IV25 3RW.
Tel. 0862-810185

North of England Mule Sheep Association Ltd
Secretary, Mrs Dorothy Bell, Tunstall House Farm, Wolsingham, Bishop Auckland, Co. Durham, DL13 3LZ.
Tel. 0388-527411

Romney Sheep Breeders' Society
David Roberts, Geneva, St Mary-in-the-Marsh, Romney Marsh, Kent, TN29 0DG.
Tel. New Romney 0679-63839

Rough Fell Sheep Breeders' Association
Mrs P. Tyson, Weasdale Farm, Newbiggin-on-Lune, Kirkby Stephen, Cumbria.
Tel. 05873-238

Ryeland Flock Book Society Ltd
Mrs Q. Jones, Westfield, Upperton, Yazor, Hereford, HR4 7BB.
Tel. 0544-310857

Shetland Flock Book Trust
J. A. Johnson, Fairview, Vidlin, Shetland.
Tel. 080-67227

Shropshire Sheep Breeders' Association
C. C. Roads, c/o McCartneys, The Cattle Market, Worcester, WR1 3NU.
Tel. 0905-612968

Suffolk Sheep Society
Miss P. Lawrence, The Sheep Centre, Malvern, Worcs. WR13 6PJ.

Swaledale Sheep Breeders' Association
R. Waggett, 2 Skelton Hall, Marske, Richmond, North Yorks.
Tel. 074-8850-280

Teeswater Sheep Breeders' Association Ltd
Mrs B. Gorst, Mutton Hall, Old Hutton, Kendal, Cumbria, LA8 0NW.

United Kingdom Finewool Register
Secretary, Miss S. Newman, Rowdens Farmhouse, Bunny Lane, Sherfield English Romsey, Hants. SO51 6FT.
Tel. 0794 884480

Welsh Agricultural Sales & Export Council
J. Arthur George, FRAgS, ACIS, c/o 32 North Parade, Aberystwyth, Dyfed.

Welsh Mountain Sheep Society (Hillflock Section)
G. Moss Jones, c/o WAOS Ltd, Brynawel, PO Box 8, Aberystwyth, Dyfed.
Tel. 0970-624011

Welsh Hill Speckled Face Sheep Society
M. Ellis, Morris, Marshall & Poole, Auctioneers, 10 Broad Street, Newtown, Powys, SY16 2LZ.
Tel. 0686-25900

Welsh Mountain Sheep Society (Pedigree Section)
Wm Jones, Prysor, Ruthin, Clwyd, LL15 2TR.

Wensleydale Longwool Sheep Breeders' Association
Mr B. Holgate, Kay Fold Farm, Ramsgreave, Blackburn, Lancs.
Tel. 0254-48152.

Whiteface Dartmoor Sheep Breeders' Association
J. E. Harris, 13 West Street, Ashburton, Devon, TQ13 7DT.
Tel. 0364-52304

RECOGNISED HALF-BRED SECTIONS

Welsh Half-bred
General Secretaries, c/o WAOS Ltd, Brynawel, PO Box 8, Aberystwyth, Dyfed.
Tel. 0970-4011

Welsh Mule Sheep Breeders' Association Ltd
General Secretaries, c/o WAOS Ltd, Brynawel, PO Box 8, Aberystwyth, Dyfed.
Tel. 0970-4011

BREEDING COMPANIES & PIGS

National Pig Breeders' Association
G. E. Welsh, 7 Rickmansworth Road, Watford, Herts, WD1 7HE.
Tel. Watford 34377
(Breeding Companies and Berkshire British Saddleback, Chester White, Duroc, Gloucestershire Old Spots, Hampshire, Landrace, Large Black, Large White, Middle White, Tamworth, Welsh.)

British Lop Pig Society
F. L. Collings, Kilmar, Pengover Road, Liskeard, Cornwall, PL14 3NW.
Tel. 0579-43198

HORSES & PONIES AND ADMINISTRATIVE & ASSOCIATED SOCIETIES

Arab Horse Society
Administration Centre, Windsor House, Ramsbury, Nr Marlborough, Wiltshire, SN8 2PE.
Tel. 0672-20782

Association of Show and Agricultural Organisations
J. N. Armitage, Esq, The Showground, Winthorpe, Newark, Notts, NG24 2NY.
Tel. 0636-702627

British Trakehner Association
Buckwood, Fulmer, Bucks, SL3 63N.
Tel. Fulmer 2606

Bransby Home of Rest for Horses
Bransby, Saxilby, Lincoln, LN1 2PH.

The British Bloodstock Agency plc
Queensberry House, Newmarket, Suffolk.
Tel. 0638-665021

British Driving Society
Mrs J. Dillon, 27 Dugard Place, Barford, Warwick, CV35 8DX.
Tel. Barford 0926-624420
Scottish Branch Secretary, Mrs E. Cornish, Easter Bavelaw, Balerno, Edinburgh EH14 7JS.
Tel. 031-449-3799

British Equine Veterinary Association
Administration Secretary, Hartham Park, Corsham, Wiltshire, SN13 0QB.
Tel. 0249-715723

British Hay & Straw Merchants' Association
F. W. Burton, Esq, 66a High Street, Potters Bar, Herts, EN6 5AB.
Tel. 0707-57171

British Morgan Horse Society
George & Dragon Hall, Mary Place, London, W11.
Tel. 071-229-8155

British Palomino Society
Mrs P. Howell, British Palomino Society, Penrhiwllan, Llandysul, Dyfed, SA44 5NZ.
Tel. 023-975-387

British Percheron Society
Alice Neaves, 76 Broad Street, Ely, Cambs, CB7 4AH.
Tel. Ely 0353-667005

British Quarter Horse Association
4th Street, National Agricultural Centre, Stoneleigh, Kenilworth, Warwicks.
Tel. 0203-696549

British Show Hack, Cob and Riding Horse Association
Mrs R. A. Smith, Rookwood, Packington Park, Meriden, Warwickshire, CV7 7HF.
Tel. 0676-23535

British Show Jumping Association
Mr Finding, The British Equestrian Centre, Kenilworth, Warwickshire.
Tel. Coventry 696516

British Show Pony Society
Mrs J. Toynton, BSPS Office, 124 Green End Road, Sawtry, Huntingdon.
Tel. 0487-831376

British Show Pony Society Scottish Branch
Mrs S. Nixon, 1 Avonmill Road, Linlithgow, West Lothian, EH49 7SQ.
Tel. 0506-843559

British Spotted Pony Society
Mrs E. C. M. Williamson, Weston Manor, Corscombe, Dorset, DT2 0PB.
Tel. 093-589-466

British Caspian Trust
(Registered Charity), Colonsay, Hampton Lovett, Droitwich, WR9 0LZ.
Tel. 029-923-399

Cleveland Bay Horse Society
J. F. Stephenson, Esq, York Livestock Centre, Murton, York.
Tel. York 489731

Dartmoor Pony Society
Mrs M. Danford, Fordans, 17 Clare Court, Newbiggen Street, Thaxted, Essex.

English Connemara Pony Society
Mrs V. Newman, 2 The Leys, Salford, Chipping Norton, Oxon, OX7 5FD.

Exmoor Pony Society
D. Mansell, Glen Fern, Waddicombe, Dulverton, Somerset, TA22 9RY.
Tel. Anstey Mills 03984-490

Federation Equestre Internationale
Bolligénstrasse 54, PO Box CH -3000, Berne 32.
Tel. 41-31-42-93-42

Fell Pony Society
Mrs Rachel H. P. Bell, Greylads Cottage, Lariston Farm, Newcastleton, Roxburghshire, TD9 0SL.
Tel. 03873-76251

Hackney Horse Society
Clump Cottage, Chitterne, Warminster, BA12 0LL.
Tel. Warminster 0985-50906

Highland Pony Society
Mr Ian W. Brown, Beechwood, Elie, Fife, KY9 1DH.
Tel. 0333-330696

Hurlingham Polo Association
J. W. M. Crisp Esq, Winterlake, Kirtlington, Oxfordshire, OX5 3HG.
Tel. 0869-50044

International League for the Protection of Horses
67a Camden High Street, London, NW1 7JL.
Tel. 071-388-1449/8333

Irish Draught Horse Society (GB)
4th Street, National Agricultural Centre, Stoneleigh Park, Kenilworth, Warwickshire, CV8 2LG.
Tel. 0203-696549

Jockey Club
Registry Office, 42 Portman Square, London, W1H 0EN.

New Forest Pony Breeding and Cattle Society
Miss D. Macnair, Beacon Cottage, Burley, Ringwood, Hants.
Tel. Burley 2272

National Pony Society
Colonel A. R. Whent, Brook House, 25 High Street, Alton, Hants, GU34 1AW.
Tel. Alton 88333

National Foaling Bank
Meretown Stud, Newport, Shropshire, TF10 8TX.
Tel. Newport 0952-811234

National Light Horse Breeding Society (HIS)
G. W. Evans, Esq, 96 High Street, Edenbridge, Kent, TN8 5AR.
Tel. Edenbridge 866277

Ponies Association (UK)
56 Green End Road, Sawtry, Huntingdon, Cambs, PE17 5VY.
Tel. 0487-830278

Pony Trekking & Riding Society of Wales
c/o Pat Morgan, 12 Sycamore Crescent, Trefechan, Merthyr Tydfil, Mid Glamorgan, CF48 2ET.
Tel. 0685-5479

Racehorse Owners' Association
42 Portman Square, London, W1H 9FF.
Tel. 071-486-6977

Riding for the Disabled Association
The Director, Avenue R, National Agricultural Centre, Kenilworth, Warwickshire.
Tel. Coventry 696510

Shire Horse Society
R. W. Bird, Esq, MBE, East of England Show, Alwalton, Peterborough.
Tel. Peterborough 234451

Suffolk Horse Society
P. Ryder-Davies, Esq, MB, BS, BVSc, MRCVS, 6 Church Street, Woodbridge, Suffolk.
Tel. Wickham Market 746534

Thoroughbred Breeders' Association
N. P. C. Musgrave, Esq, Stanstead House, The Avenue, Newmarket, Suffolk, CB8 9AA.
Tel. Newmarket 661321

Welsh Pony and Cob Society
J. Pritchard, 6 Chalybeate Street, Aberystwyth, Dyfed, SY23 1HS.
Tel. Aberystwyth 617501

MISCELLANEOUS

Masters of Foxhounds Association
A. H. B. Hart, Esq, Parsloes Cottage, Bagendon, Cirencester, Glos.
Tel. North Cerney 470

Royal College of Veterinary Surgeons
32 Belgrave Square, London, SW1X 8QP.
Tel. 071-235-4971

The Worshipful Company of Ferriers
H. W. H. Ellis, Esq, FCA, 37 The Uplands, Loughton, Essex, IG10 1NO.
Tel. 081-508-6242

The Worshipful Company of Loriners
50 Cheyne Avenue, London, E18 2DR.
Tel. 081-989-0652

The Worshipful Company of Saddlers
40 Saddlers Hall, Gutter Lane, Cheapside, London, EC2V 6BR.
Tel. 071-726-8661

AGRICULTURAL MUSEUMS IN SCOTLAND

Intending visitors are advised to establish times of opening before making a special journey.

Angus Folk Museum
Kirkwynd Cottages, Glamis, Angus, DD8 1RT.
Tel. 030784-288

Auchindrain Open Air Museum of Country Life
Nr Inveraray, Argyll, PA32 8XN.
Tel. 04995-235

Border Country Life Museum
Thirlestane Castle, Lauder, Berwickshire, TD2 6RU.
Tel. 05782-430

Corrigall Farm Museum
Harray, Orkney.
Tel. 085677-411

Ellisland Farm
Holywood, Dumfriesshire, DG2 0RP.
Tel. 038774-426

Highland Folk Museum
Duke Street, Kingussie, Inverness-shire, PH21 1JG.
Tel. 05402-307

Isle of Arran Heritage Museum
Rosaburn, Brodick, Isle of Arran, KA27 8DP.
Tel. 0770-2636

Ladycroft Farm Museum
Elchies, Nr Archiestown, Moray.
Tel. 03406-274

Lhaidhay Croft Museum
Dunbeath, Caithness, KW6 6EH.
Tel. 05932-208

Livingston Mill Farm
Millfield, Kirkton, Livingston, West Lothian, EH54 1AR.
Tel. 0506-414957

North East of Scotland Agricultural Heritage Centre
Aden Country Park, Mintlaw, Nr Peterhead, Aberdeenshire, AB4 8LD.
Tel. 0771-22807

Pitmedden Museum of Farming Life, Garden and Grounds
(National Trust for Scotland)
Gordon, Pitmedden, Ellon, Aberdeenshire, AB4 0PD.
Tel. 06513-2352

Ruskie Farm and Landscape Museum
Dunaverig, Ruskie, Thornhill, by Stirling, FK8 3QW.
Tel. 078685-277

Scone Palace
Perth, PH2 6BD.
Tel. 0738-52300

Scottish Agricultural Museum
(National Museums of Scotland) Ingliston, Newbridge, Nr Edinburgh (in Royal Highland Showground).
Tel. 031-333-2674
or contact
National Museums of Scotland, Queen Street, Edinburgh, EH2 1JD.
Tel. 031-225-7534

Tingwall Agricultural Museum
Veensgarth, Gott, Shetland, ZE2 9SB.
Tel. 059584-344
For additional museums it is suggested that visitors consult local Tourist Information Centres or a guide such as *Scottish Museums and Galleries Guide*, Polygon/Scottish Museums Council, 1986.

SCOTLAND'S LEADING AGRICULTURAL SHOWS

January

Kilpatrick Foal Show.
Tel. 041-779-1236

February

Aberdeen Spring Show.
Tel. 0224-311362

April

National Stallion Show.
Tel. 0292-266768

Kilmaurs Show.
Tel. 0563-44699

Ochiltree Show.
Tel. 029-07-330

Beith Show.
Tel. 050-55-2563

Ayr Show.
Tel. 0292-266600

Dundonald Show.
Tel. 0563-830330

May

Neilston Show.
Tel. 041-881-1980

Catrine Show.
Tel. 0290-51433

Dumbarton Show.
Tel. 03860-60481

Kilmacolm Show.

Lanark County Horse Show.

Dalry Show.
Tel. 029-483-2112

Dalrymple Show.
Tel. 0292-43793

Fife Show.

Stonehouse Show.

Lesmahagow Show.
Tel. 055-582-255

Drymen Show.
Tel. 036-086-328

Stewarton Show.
Tel. 0560-84767

New Cummnock Show.
Tel. 0290-38304

Royal Northern Beef Event
Tel. 0224-311362

June

Houston Show.
Tel. 0505-612422

Campsie Show.
Tel. 0360-311262

Newmilns Show.
Tel. 0563-820262

West Fife.
Tel. 0383-881111

Carsphairn Show

Largs Show.
Tel. 0475-674576

Stirling Show.
Tel. 0259-60432

Kilbarchan Show.
Tel. 050-57-2185

Royal Highland Show, Ingliston, Newbridge, Midlothian.
Tel. 031-333-3211

Alyth Show.
Tel. 0250-3211

Scotcrop '90
Tel. 031-333-2444

July

Dunblane Show.
Tel. 0786-841227

Haddington Show.
Tel. 0368-62376

Royal Show, Stoneleigh, Warwickshire.
Tel. 0203-555-100

Echt Show
Tel. 03306-276

Dalkeith Show.
Tel. 0506-845084

Great Yorkshire Show, Harrogate

New Deer Show.
Tel. 07714-675

St Boswells Show
Tel. 0835-22214

Ardoch Show.
Tel. 078688-263

Biggar Show.
Tel. 0555-3305

Angus Show.
Tel. 02412-498

Stranraer Show.
Tel. 0776-3539

Caithness Show.
Tel. 084-783-614

Westside Show.

Kelso Show.
Tel. 0573-24188

East Kilbride Show.
Tel. 035-73-392

Banchory Show.
Tel. 0224 733565

Game Conservancy Scottish Fair.
Tel. 0383-872863

August

Turriff Show.
Tel. 046-65-267

Nairn Show.
Tel. 030-94-491

Wigtown Show.

Black Isle Show.
Tel. 0463-233957

Stewartry Show.
Tel. 0556-3261

Kintyre Show.
Tel. 0586-52472

Perth Show.
Tel. 0738-23780

Dumfries Show.
Tel. 0387-53425

Lorn Show.
Tel. 0631 -631 58

Duns Show.

Helensburgh Combined Show.
Tel. 0436-831245

Keith Show.
Tel. 0542-34220

Arran Show.
Tel. 077-087-241

Bute Show.
Tel. 070-083-692

Carnwath Show.

Craigie Show.
Tel. Tarbolton 541210

Islay Show.
Tel. 049-681-555

Granton Show.
Tel. 0343-7492.

Salen Show, Mull.
Tel. 06803-338

Kinross Show.
Tel. Milnathort 62816

Aberfeldy Show.
Tel. 0887-20321

Mid Argyll Show.
Tel. 0546-86660

Orkney Show.

Fenwick Show.
Tel. 0563-37849

Peebles Show.
Tel. 0721-20541

Kilmuir Show.
Tel. 047-052-312

Avondale Show.
Tel. 0357-20211

Chapelton Show.
Tel. 0357-21070

Coylton Show.
Tel. 0292-266766

Abington Show.
Tel. 0397-3819

Muirkirk Show.
Tel. 0290-61335

Moffat Show.
Tel. 05762-3549

Holm Show.
Tel. 038-73-632

Aberdeen Clydesdale Show

September
Strathaven Exposition.
Tel. 0357-21623

Dalmally Show.
Tel. 083-82-277

Aberdeen Goat Show.
Tel. 0224-311362

Yarrow Show.

Dairy Event at NAC.
Tel. 0203-555-100

Langholm Show.
Tel. 038-73-80222

October

ScotGrow,
W. W. Romanis, 17 Grosvenor Crescent, Edinburgh.
Tel. 031-337-4333

Tarbolton Show.
Tel. Tarbolton 541210

November
Scottish Agricultural Winter Fair,
Tel. 031-333-2444

December

Smithfield Show, Earl's Court, London.
December.
Tel. 01 -235-0315

(At the time of going to press many of the show dates had yet to be verified.)

LEADING HIGHLAND GAMES

June
Aberdeen Highland Games.
Secretary: D. Welch, Director of Leisure and Recreation Department, City of Aberdeen District Council, St Nicholas House, Broad Street, Aberdeen.
Tel. 0224-642121

July
Dundee Highland Games.
Secretary: Susan Gillan, Leisure and Recreation Department, City of Dundee District Council, 353 Clepington Road, Dundee, DD3 8PL.
Tel. 0382-23141

Balloch (Loch Lomond) Highland Games.
Secretary: John Martin, 42 Park Avenue, Balloch, G83 8JS.
Tel. 0389-52288

Luss (Loch Lomond) Highland Games.
Secretary: J. F. Nicol, 47a Colquhoun Square, Helensburgh, G84 9LQ.
Tel. 0436-2919

August
Inverkeithing Highland Games.
Secretary: M. McGregor, 2 Milton Green, Dunfermline, KY12 7PS.
Tel. 0383-28462

Aboyne Highland Games.
Secretary: A. J. Coutts, MBE, 15 Golf Crescent, Aboyne.
Tel. 0339-2187

Perth Highland Games.
Secretary: A. Rettie, Limetree Cottage, Pitcairngreen, Perth, PH1 3LP.
Tel. 0738-83754

Crieff Highland Gathering.
Secretary: A. Rettie, Limetree Cottage, Pitcairngreen, Perth, PH1 3LP.
Tel. 0738-83754

September
Braemar Gathering.
Secretary: W. A. Meston, Balcriech, Ballater, AB3 5UH.
Tel. 0338-55377

Pitiochry Highland Games.
Secretary: D. McLauchlan, Easter Auchlatt, Pitlochry, PH16 5JL.
Tel. 0796-2207

For further information concerning Highland Games/ Gatherings throughout Scotland, contact: Andrew Rettie, Limetree Cottage, Pitcairngreen, Perth, PH1 3LP.
Tel. 0738-83754.

USEFUL INFORMATION

SCOTTISH BORDER FESTIVALS

Hawick Common Riding
Mr F. Scott.
Tel. Hawick (0450) 73178

Selkirk Common Riding
Mr J. Cruikshank.
Tel. Selkirk (0750) 21344

Melrose Summer Festival
Mrs Henderson.
Tel. Melrose (089682) 2885

Peebles Beltane Festival
Mr A. Beveridge.
Tel. Peebles (0721) 20637

Galashiels Braw Lads' Gathering
Miss M. Keith.
Tel. Galashiels (0896) 2045

Jedburgh Callants' Festival
Mr G. Jeffrey.
Tel. Jedburgh (0835) 62724

Duns Summer Festival

Kelso Civic Week
Mr Allan.
Tel. Kelso (0573) 24756

Langholm Common Riding
Mr Hill.
Tel. 03873-80428

Lauder Common Riding
Mr McLaren.
Tel. Lauder (05782) 589

Coldstream Civic Week
Mr Budge.
Tel. Coldstream (0890) 2951

INTERNATIONAL SHEEP DOG SOCIETY

DATES AND VENUES FOR 1990 NATIONAL AND INTERNATIONAL TRIALS

Ireland
25th to 27th July, Wexford, Eire.
England
19th, 20th and 21st August, Rydal, Ambleside, Cumbria.
Scotland
1st to 3rd August, Inverness.
Wales
8th to 10th August, Dolgellau, Gwynedd.
International
12th to 14th September, Carmichael, Lanarkshire.

VISITORS' CENTRE-HERITAGE

SCOTTISH FORESTRY HERITAGE PROJECT
at Landmark Visitor Centre, Carrbridge, Inverness-shire, PH23 3AJ.
Tel. 047-984-613

DIGGING UP THE ROAD-BRITISH TELECOM

Those concerned with excavation works can obtain information on the location of BT underground plant from British Telecom Underground Plant Enquiries.
Dial 100 and ask for Freefone 111.

EDINBURGH FESTIVAL
USEFUL TELEPHONE NUMBERS

Edinburgh Festival Society Limited: 031-226-4001.
Edinburgh Film Festival: 031-228-6382.
Edinburgh Military Tattoo: 031-225-1188.
Festival Fringe Society: 031-226-5257.

SCOTTISH AIRPORTS

Aberdeen: 0224-722331.
Benbecula: 0870-2051.
Dundee: 0382-643242.
Edinburgh: 031-333-1000.
Glasgow: 041-887-1111.
Inverness: 0463-232471.
Islay (Port Ellen): 0496-2361.
Kirkwall: 0856-2421.
London (Gatwick): 0293-28822.
London (Heathrow): 081-759-4321.
Prestwick: 0292-79822.
Stornoway: 0851-2256.
Sumburgh: 0950-60654.
Tiree (Scarinish): 08792-456.
Wick: 0955-2215.

STRAW AND STUBBLE BURNING CODE

The Government will introduce a ban on straw and stubble burning in the autumn of 1992. At present there is no intention of introducing a ban in Scotland. But cereals committee convener, David Jack has emphasised the need to follow the straw burning code. The details are as follows:–

Before Burning:

1. Make a fire break at least ten metres wide by one of the following methods:
(a) Remove the straw from a ten metres strip around the perimeter of the field and then cultivate or rotovate this strip thoroughly or plough a minimum of nine furrows.

(b) Burn the straw around the perimeter one swath at a time in the early morning when the dew is on the ground.

2. Consult the fire brigade in advance, prepare directions to the site of burning.

3. Notify your neighbours and, if burning near a residential area, consult your District Environmental Health Department.

4. Listen to the weather forecast and reassess your programme if there is likely to be an increase in wind strength or a change in wind direction.

5. Where fire could damage the public highway or where smoke is likely create a hazard to drivers.

When Burning:

1. Put an experienced hand in charge. Never leave the fire unattended.

2. Limit the area of burning to a controllable size.

3. Start early in the day.

4. Burn against the wind. If this is impracticable, burn a strip at least 30 metres wide across the down wind end of the field before starting to burn with the wind.

5. Ensure the staff is available, and make sure that you can get further help for use in an emergency.

6. If the fire is out of control, call the fire brigade immediately. Meet the brigade at the roadside and show them the best way to the fire.

7. Remember, that a strong fire creates its own wind current. This may cause the fire to develop in unexpected ways.

8. The fire must be completely out before you leave the field. Check for smouldering and return later in order to make sure.

Wayleaves

By Paul S. Blacklock

Landowners will often have to deal with wayleaves over their land, whether by electric, water, telephone or gas utilities. The general principle is that all utilities will pay compensation for actual damage done, whether to the land, crops or business. Water authorities are singular in that they pay nothing for the use of the land; others pay a 'rent'.

While the individual landowner is free to negotiate with the appropriate body, it is found in practice more convenient for all concerned for the representative bodies (SLF and NFUS in Scotland) to carry out national negotiations. Individuals are free to negotiate if they feel circumstances warrant more 'rent'.

Set out below are the rates for electricity until Spring 1991.

SCOTTISH POWER plc RENT & COMPENSATION PAYMENTS – APPLICABLE AT WHITSUNDAY 1990

DISTRIBUTION LINES

RENT Per Annum	
For each single pole	£0.30
For each 'A' or 'H' pole	£0.40
For each stay	£0.20
For each double steel pole structure without stays	£0.50
For each double steel structure with stays	£1.40
For any length of overhead electric line where no supports are erected on the land	£0.12
For any electric line laid underground, each 100 yards route length or part thereof	£0.22

Rates for permanent servitudes to be the subject of separate negotiation

	Arable Land p.a.	Enclosed Permanent Pasture p.a.	Grazing & Hill Land p.a.
COMPENSATION			
Single pole	£ 7.00	£ 1.40	£ 0.25
'A' or 'H' or strutted pole	£11.16	£ 2.23	£ 0.48
Initial Stay	£ 8.21	£ 1.90	£ 0.48
Additional Stay	£ 4.10	£ 1.00	£ 0.25

Poles, stays or struts in hedgerows or fences - half above rates

DOUBLE STEEL POLE STRUCTURES

Straight line without stays	£13.04	£ 2.60	£ 0.34
Straight line with stays	£20.84	£ 4.18	£ 0.48
Angle with stays	£31.28	£ 6.26	£ 0.61

TRANSMISSION LINES

RENT	Arable Land p.a.	Enclosed Permanent Pasture p.a.	Grazing & Hill Land p.a.
For each tower with base dimensions over concrete at ground level up to:			
15 ft square	£ 0.64	£ 0.54	£ 0.54
25 ft square	£ 1.60	£ 1.01	£ 1.01
35 ft square	£ 2.36	£ 1.34	£ 1.34
45 ft square	£ 3.24	£ 2.01	£ 2.01
Over 45 ft square	£ 4.48	£ 2.66	£ 2.66

Lines only twelve pence per annum payable to owner.

COMPENSATION

Towers with base dimensions over concrete at ground level up to:-

	Arable Land p.a.	Enclosed Permanent Pasture p.a.	Grazing & Hill Land p.a.
10ft square	£13.04	£ 1.64	£ 0.65
12′ 6″	£18.32	£ 2.28	£ 0.65
15ft square	£20.84	£ 2.60	£ 0.65
18ft square	£25.96	£ 3.24	£ 0.70
24ft square	£33.72	£ 4.24	£ 0.70
30ft square	£41.24	£ 5.16	£ 0.75
40ft square	£52.88	£ 6.60	£ 0.80
50ft square	£63.52	£ 7.96	£ 0.90

Note:

1 Intermediate sizes to receive the next higher figure. Larger sizes to be separately negotiated.

HYDRO-ELECTRIC PROPOSED WAYLEAVE PAYMENT RATES EFFECTIVE FROM MAY 1990

1 POLES AND STAYS

(a) Arable

Single pole	£7.30
Double pole	£11.56
Stay	£8.41

(b) Non Arable

Single pole	£0.35
Double pole	£0.50
Stay	£0.47

2 TOWERS

(a) Arable

Under 1O ft square	(3.0 metres)	£13.68
Under 12.5 ft square	(3.8 metres)	£18.96
Under 15 ft square	(4.5 metres)	£21.48
Under 20 ft square	(6.0 metres)	£27.56
Under 25 ft square	(7.5 metres)	£35.32
Under 30 ft squcare	(9.0 metres)	£43.60
Under 35 ft square	(10.5 metres)	£49.48
Under 40 ft square	(12.0 metres)	£56.12
Under 45 ft square	(13.5 metres)	£61.68
Under 50 ft square	(15.0 metres)	£68.00
50 ft square and over	(15.0 metres) to be individually negotiated	

(b) Non Arable

Under 15 ft square	(4.5 metres)	£0.96
Under 25 ft square	(7.5 metres)	£1.60
Under 35 ft square	(10.5 metres)	£2.16
Under 45 ft square	(13.5 metres)	£3.08
45 ft square and over	(13.5 metres)	£4.00

3 UNDERGROUND CABLES

Rates per 100 metre or part thereof £0.25

4 OVERHEAD CROSSINGS £0.12

British Gas Scotland

Landowners and Tenants requiring information on Wayleaves or in respect of pipelines on their land or any other works carried out by British Gas should contact the Wayleave Section on 031-559-5000.

BUSINESS GOODS AND SERVICES

ANIMAL FEEDS

BOCM SILCOCK LTD
Wright Street,
Renfrew, PA4 8AH.
Tel. **041-887-1288**
and
Penrith Industrial Estate
Penrith, CA11 9EH
Tel. **0768-62064**

CONSERVATION

Scottish Conservation Projects
Balallan House,
24 Allan Park,
Stirling FK8 2QG
Tel. 0786-79697
Fax. 0786-65359

Scottish Conservation Projects promotes the practical involvement of people in conserving the wildlife and scenic heritage of Scotland. Construct footpaths, create wildlife habitats, build drystane dykes, carry out fencing, renovate stone bothies, stabilise river banks and undertake tree-planting and woodland management. Our practical work and advisory service extends throughout Scotland.

We have offices in Edinburgh, Glasgow, Falkirk and Doune with north-east office opening shortly.

Scottish Division
Old Sauchie, Sauchieburn, Stirling FK7 9QG
Telephone Bannockburn (0786) 811721
Facsimile (0786) 814124

Forest management and contract services, supply of plants, timber purchasing, purchase of planting land, Farm forestry advisory and contract services.

PATHCRAFT LIMITED
70 MAIN STREET
DOUNE

Perthshire FK16 6BW
Telephone: **(0786) 841915**
Specialists in Upland
Footpath Construction
and Erosion Control

FARM BUSINESS CONSULTANTS

David Anderson & Company

58 John Street,
Penicuik,
Midlothian EH26 8NE
Tel. 0968 78465

Peter Pitchford or Francis Mordaunt.
The Company provides a whole range of farm business consultancy services from simple budget and cash flow preparation to full executive management of farms and estates.

FINANCE

LAND AGENTS

USEFUL ABBREVIATIONS

ABRO Animal Breeding Research Organisation
ACC Agricultural Credit Corporation
ADAS Agricultural Development and Advisory Service
ADMMB Aberdeen & District Milk Marketing Board
ADP Agricultural Development Programme
ADRA Animal Diseases Research Association
AEA Agricultural Engineers' Association
AFRC Agricultural and Food Research Council
APRS Association for the Protection of Rural Scotland
ATB Agricultural Training Board

BAA British Agrochemicals Association
BAB Bureau de l'Agriculture Britannique *(UK Agri-cultural Bureau in Brussels)*
BAC British Agricultural Council
BAGMA British Agricultural and Garden Machinery Association
BAEC British Agricultural Export Council
BASC British Association for Shooting and Conservation
BCGA British Compressed Gases Association
BCPC British Crop Protection Council
BEA British Egg Association
BEIC British Egg Industry Council
BFSS(S) British Field Sports Society (Scotland)
BGLA British Growers Look Ahead Exhibition *(main UK Horticuftural Exhibition held NEC Birmingham)*
BOCM British Oil and Cake Mills *(BOCM Silcock Ltd)*
BSE Bovine Spongiform Encephalopathy
BSI British Standards Institution
BSRAE British Society for Research in Agricultural Engineering
BST Bovine Somatotrophin
BST British Summer Time
BTA British Trout Association
BVA British Veterinary Association
BWGS Broadleaved Woodland Grant Scheme
BWMB British Wool Marketing Board

CAP Common Agricultural Policy *(basic principles on which farm policy was set out in Treaty of Rome to: (a) ensure a fair standard of living to those working on the land; (b) to ensure realistic prices to consumers)*
CASE Co-operative Awards in Science and Engineering
CBI Confederation of British Industry
CC Countryside Commission
CC Community Charge (Poll Tax)
CDB Co-operative Development Board
CEA Confederation of Agricultural Producers
CEC Council of European Communities
CEJA European Young Farmers' Council
CEPFA European Training and Promotion Centre for Farming and Rural Life
CGT Capital Gains Tax
CLA Country Landowners' Association *(English equivalent of SLF)*
COGECA Farmers' Co-operative organisation in the EEC
COPA Committee of Professional Agricultural Organisations *(in effect the joint farmers' union of the EC)*
COSLA Convention of Scottish Local Authorities
COSHH Control of Substances Hazardous to Health
CPO Compulsory Purchase Order
CRL Co-responsibility Levy (Cereals)
CSCT Central Scotland Countryside Trust
CSTS Craft Skills Training Scheme *(referred to in ATB literature)*
CSF Classical Swine Fever
CTT Capital Transfer Tax

DA Disadvantaged Areas
DAC District Apprenticeship Committees *(ATB Local Training Committee – likely to change its name)*
DAFS Department of Agriculture and Fisheries for Scotland *(Government Department dealing with agriculture and fisheries for Scotland)*
DIS Direct Intervention Scheme *(Potato Marketing support system)*

DV District Valuer
DVO Divisional Veterinary Officer *(Local Department-vets dealing with animal/testing/eradication of disease)*

EAPR European Association for Potato Research
ECC Electricity Consultative Council
ECU European Currency Unit
EEC European Economic Community
EETC Edinburgh Exhibition and Trade Centre
EFG Economic Forestry Group
EHS Experimental Horticultural Station
ELGA European Liaison Group for Agriculture
EMS European Monetary System
ENFU English NFU *NFU of England and Wales)*
ESA Environmentally Sensitive Area
ESCA East of Scotland College of Agriculture

FAC Federation of Agricultural Co-operatives
FAO Food and Agricultural Organisation
FEOGA/EAGGF European Agricultural Guidance and Guarantee Fund *(This is the English translation – FEOGA is how it would be abbreviated in French)*
FFB Food from Britain
FFWAG Farming and Forestry Wildlife Advisory Group
FMA Fertiliser Manufacturers' Association
FWT Farming and Wildlife Trust

GATT General Agreement on Tariffs and Trade
GC Game Conservancy
GIUS Glasshouse Investigational Unit for Scotland *(Research Centre for protected crops work at Auchincruive, Nr. Ayr, attached to West of Scotland Agricultural College)*
GREEN POUND Artificial rates of exchange which apply to farm products within the EEC

HDC Horticultural Development Council
HFRO Hill Farming Research Organisation
HGCA Home Grown Cereals Authority *(Statutory Body financed by farmers, processors, trade involved and market information R. & D. promotion, etc.)*
HIDB Highlands and Islands Development Board
HLCA Hill Livestock Compensatory Amount *(subsidy paid to livestock producers in less favoured areas)*
HMSO Her Majesty's Stationery Office
HSE Health and Safety Executive *(Government Department who carry out health and safety operations and policy on farms)*
HTA Horticultural Trades Association

IBAP Intervention Board for Agricultural Produce
IDP Integrated Development Programme
IFA Irish Farmers' Association
IFAP International Federation of Agricultural Producers
IHR Institute and Horticultural Research
IMF International Monetary Fund
IOH Institute of Horticulture
ITE Institute of Terrestrial Ecology
IAAS Institute of Auctioneers and Appraisers in Scotland

LFA Less Favoured Areas *(term used for disadvantaged areas, i.e. mainly hill and upland farms. These areas receive special support arrangements for livestock, grants, etc.)*
LPR Land Price Review
LSU Livestock Unit
LTA Land Trusts Association

MAFF Ministry of Agriculture Food and Fisheries
MCA Monetary Compensatory Amount *(Green Pound – Exchange Rates enabling EEC to maintain common support price structure for certain commodities) (Negative MCA – Subsidy of Imports – Tax on exports) (Positive MCA – Tax on Imports – Subsidy of exports)*
MGA Mushroom Growers' Association

MLC Meat and Livestock Commission *(Government Body financed by farmers and meat industry: deals with research, promotion/support arrangements, i.e. variable meat premiums, for meat industry)*
MMB Milk Marketing Board
MPE Meat Promotion Executive

NAGS National Association of Group Secretaries *(The Secretary's Union – registered as an official Trade Union)*
NCC Nature Conservancy Council
NCC National Consumer Council
NEDO National Economic Development Office
NFU National Farmers' Union of England and Wales
NFUS National Farmers' Union of Scotland
NHEB North of Scotland Hydro Electric Board
NOAH National Office of Animal Health
NoSCA North of Scotland College of Agriculture
NOSMMB North of Scotland Milk Marketing Board
NPBA National Pig Breeders' Association
NSA National Sheep Association
NSDO National Seed Development Organisation
NTS National Trust for Scotland

OECD Organisation for Economic Co-operation and Development
OS Ordnance Survey

PBI Plant Breeding International
PCN Potato Cyst Nemstode *(a potato disease)*
PICKUP Professional Industrial and Commercial updating
PMB Potato Marketing Board *(body which regulates the production/marketing of potatoes. Financed by Statutory Levy from producers)*
PRB Plant Royalty Bureau

R & D Research and Development
RDC Red Deer Commission
RHASS Royal Highland and Agricultural Society of Scotland *(organisers of the Royal Highland Show)*
RICS Royal Institute of Chartered Surveyors
ROSPA Royal Society for the Prevention of Accidents
RSABI Royal Scottish Agricultural Benevolent Institution
RSFS Royal Scottish Forestry Society
RURAL Responsible use of resources in Agriculture and on the land

SAC Scottish Agricultural Colleges
SAGS Scottish Association of Group Secretaries
SAI Scottish Agricultural Industries Ltd
SAOS Scottish Agricultural Organisation Society *(Scottish Body of Farming Co-operatives)*
SARIs Scottish Agricultural Research Industries
SASC Scottish Agricultural Securities Corporation
SAWB Scottish Agricultural Wages Board
SAYFC
Scottish Association of Young Farmers' Clubs
SCAE Scottish Centre of Agricultural Engineering
SCCS Standing Conference on Countryside Sports
SCDI Scottish Council Development and Industry
SCOTGROW Scottish National Horticultural Trade Exhibition organised by the NFUS.
SCP Scottish Conservation Projects
SCRI Scottish Crop Research Institute
SDA Severely Disadvantaged Areas
SDA Scottish Development Agency
SDD Scottish Development Department
SECC Scottish Exhibition and Conference Centre
SEPD Scottish Economic Planning Department
SFPE Scottish Food Promotion Executive
SIAE Scottish Institute of Agricultural Engineering
SIO Scottish Information Office
SLC Scottish Law Commission
SLF Scottish Landowners' Federation *(body representing landowners only)*
SLIG Scottish Landscape Industry Group
SMMB Scottish Milk Marketing Board
SMU Support Measurement Unit
SNSA Scottish Nuclear Stock Association *(a body designed to propagate new plant material for certification)*
SPTA Scottish Potato Trade Association
SQBLA Scottish Quality Beef and Lamb Association
SRLA Scottish Recreational Land Association
SSCR Scottish Society for Crop Research
SSGA Scottish Salmon Growers' Association
SSPDC Scottish Seed Potato Development Council
SSSI Site of Special Scientific Interest
STB Scottish Tourist Board
STM Supplementary Trade Mechanism *(EC. A device for securing financial integration of new states like Spain and Portugal)*
STUC Scottish Trades Union Congress
SWL Scottish Woodland Limited
SWT Scottish Wildlife Trust

TFA Tenant Farmers' Association (England and Wales)
TGUK Timber Growers (United Kingdom) Limited
TUFF Technical Updating for farmers *(an educational initiative)*

UFU Ulster Farmers' Union
UKASTA United Kingdom Agricultural Supply Trade Association
UKDA United Kingdom Dairy Association

VPS Variable Premium *Certified Variable Slaughter premium paid to support cattle producers – part paid by UK Government)*
VRA Voluntary Restraint Agreements
VTSC Virus Tested Stem Cutting Growers Association

WAGBI Wildlife Association of Great Britain and Ireland
WFU Women's Farming Union
WSC West of Scotland College
WWF World Wildlife Fund

EUROPEAN ORGANISATIONS

AGB Arbeitsgemeinschaft der Grunde Besitzwerbande *(German SLF)*
CEA Confederation of European Agriculture
ELGA European Liaison Group for Agriculture
ELO European Landowning Organisations Group
FNPA Federation Nationale de la Propriete Agricole *(French SLF)*

COMMON MARKET CONTACTS

AGRICULTURAL REPRESENTATIVES IN LONDON

Country	Address / Contact	Telephone
Belgium	Belgian Embassy, 103-105 Eaton Square, London SW1W 9AB. *Contact:* J. Van Mullem, Agricultural Counsellor.	01-235 4414
Denmark	Royal Danish Embassy, 55 Sloane Street, London SW1X 9SR. (Agric. Section) *Contact:* Erik Klindt Andersen, Agricultural Counsellor.	01-235 1630
France	French Embassy, 21-24 Grosvenor Place, London SW1X 7HU. *Contact:* Ph. Balny, Agricultural Attaché.	01-235 7080
Germany, Federal Republic of	Embassy of the Federal Republic of Germany, 23 Belgrave Square, Chesham Place, London SW1X 8PZ. *Contact:* Dr. Richard Peters, 1st Counsellor (Agriculture)	01-235 5033
Greece	Greek Embassy, 1a Holland Park, London W11 3TP. *Contact:* T. Karavais, Commercial Counsellor	01-727 8040, Ext. 240
Republic of Ireland	Irish Embassy, 17 Grosvenor Place, London SW1X 7HR. *Contact:* H. G. Foster, Counsellor (Agriculture).	01-235 2171
Italy	Italian Embassy, 14 Three Kings Yard, Davies Street, London W1Y 2EH. *Contact:* Enrico Augelli Head of Economic Dept.	01-629 8200
Luxembourg	Luxembourg Embassy, 27 Wilton Crescent, London SW1X 8SD.	01-235 6961
Netherlands	Royal Netherlands Embassy, 38 Hyde Park Gate, London SW7 5DP. *Contact:* D. Vries, Agricultural Counsellor; R. A. Bosch, Assistant Agricultural Attaché.	01-584 5040

U.K. REPRESENTATIVES IN EEC COUNTRIES

Country	Address / Contact	Telephone
Belgium	British Embassy Rue Joseph II, 28 Brussels 1040. *Contact:* I. L. Blackley, (see Netherlands)	02 217 9000
Denmark	British Embassy, 36/38/40 Kastelsvej, DK-2100, Copenhagen. *Contact:* S. Sadowski, 1st Secretary (Agriculture, Fisheries).	(01) 14 4600
France	British Embassy, 35 rue du Faubourg St-Honoré, 75383 Paris Cedex 08. *Contact:* B. K. Timms, Counsellor (Agriculture and Economics).	266-9142
Germany	British Embassy, Friedrich-Ebert-Allee 77, 5300 Bonn 1. *Contact:* P. Elliott, 1st Secretary (Agriculture).	0228 23-40-61
Greece	British Embassy, Ploutarchou Street 1, Athens 139.	Athens 736211
Italy	British Embassy, Via XX Settembre 80A, 00187 Roma. *Contact:* D. B. A. Evans, 1st Secretary (Agriculture).	4755441/4755551
Luxembourg	British Embassy, 28 Boulevard Royal, Luxembourg, Grand Duchy of Luxembourg. *Contact: See* Netherlands.	29864/66
Netherlands	British Embassy, Lange Voorhout 10, 2514 ED, The Hague. *Contact:* I. L. Blackley, 1st Secretary (Agriculture).	(070) 64 58 00
Republic of Ireland	British Embassy, 33 Merrion Road, Dublin 4. *Contact:* J. J. Beale, Esq., 1st Secretary (Agriculture/E.C.C.).	695211

IMPERIAL AND METRIC EQUIVALENTS

CONVERSION TABLES

Pounds to kilograms

lbs.	lbs. or kilograms	kilograms
2.205	1	0.454
4.49	2	0.907
6.614	3	1.361
8.819	4	1.814
11.023	5	2.268
13.228	6	2.722
15.432	7	3.175
17.637	8	3.629
19.842	9	4.082
22.046	10	4.536

Miles to kilometres

Miles	Miles or kilometres	kilometres
0.621	1	1.609
1.243	2	3.219
1.864	3	4.828
2.486	4	6.437
3.107	5	8.047
3.728	6	9.656
4.350	7	11.265
4.971	8	12.875
5.592	9	14.484
6.214	10	16.093

AREA

Square feet to square metres

Square feet	Square feet or Square metres	Square metres
10.764	1	0.093
21.528	2	0.186
32.292	3	0.279
43.056	4	0.372
53.820	5	0.465
65.583	6	0.557
75.347	7	0.650
86.111	8	0.743
96.875	9	0.836
107.639	10	0.929

CAPACITY

Cubic feet to cubic metres

cu. ft.	cu. ft. or cu. m.	cubic metres
35.315	1	0.028
70.629	2	0.057
105.944	3	0.085
141.259	4	0.113
176.573	5	0.142
211.888	6	0.170
247.203	7	0.198
282.517	8	0.227
317.832	9	0.255
353.147	10	0.283

Acres to Hectares

Acres	Acres or Hectares	Hectares
24.71	10	4.05
49.42	20	8.09
74.13	30	12.14
98.84	40	16.19
123.55	50	20.23
148.26	60	24.28
172.97	70	28.33
197.68	80	32.37
222.40	90	36.42
247.11	100	40.47

Gallons to litres

Gallons	Gallons or Litres	Litres
0.220	1	4.546
0.440	2	9.092
0.660	3	13.638
0.880	4	18.184
1.100	5	22.730
1.320	6	27.276
1.540	7	31.822
1.760	8	36.368
1.980	9	40.914
2.200	10	45.460

LB/ACRE

converted to kilograms per hectare

lb/ac	kg/ha
10 =	11.2
15 =	16.8
20 =	22.4
25 =	28.0
30 =	33.6
40 =	44.8
50 =	56.0
60 =	67.2
70 =	78.4
80 =	89.6
90 =	100.8
100 =	112.0

CWT/ACRE

converted to kilograms per hectare

cwt/ac	kg/ha
1 =	125.5
2 =	251.0
3 =	376.0
4 =	502.1
5 =	627.7
10 =	1255.4
20 =	2510.8
25 =	3138.5
35 =	4393.9
40 =	5021.6
45 =	5649.3
50 =	6277.0

TON/ACRE

converted to tonnes per hectare

t/ac	tonne/ha
3 =	7.5
4 =	10.0
5 =	12.5
10 =	25.1
15 =	37.6
20 =	50.2
25 =	62.7
30 =	75.3

Index of Advertisers

Desk Diary 1991

Time-tested craftsmanship and the latest production technology are combined to give all Letts products unrivalled quality
Made in Great Britain by Charles Letts & Co Ltd

Summary Calendar

1990

January					
Monday	1	8	15	22	29
Tuesday	2	9	16	23	30
Wednesday	3	10	17	24	31
Thursday	4	11	18	25	
Friday	5	12	19	26	
Saturday	6	13	20	27	
Sunday	7	14	21	28	
Week No.	1	2	3	4	5

February					
Monday		5	12	19	26
Tuesday		6	13	20	27
Wednesday		7	14	21	28
Thursday	1	8	15	22	
Friday	2	9	16	23	
Saturday	3	10	17	24	
Sunday	4	11	18	25	
Week No.	5	6	7	8	9

March					
Monday		5	12	19	26
Tuesday		6	13	20	27
Wednesday		7	14	21	28
Thursday	1	8	15	22	29
Friday	2	9	16	23	30
Saturday	3	10	17	24	31
Sunday	4	11	18	25	
Week No.	9	10	11	12	13

July						
Monday		2	9	16	23	30
Tuesday		3	10	17	24	31
Wednesday		4	11	18	25	
Thursday		5	12	19	26	
Friday		6	13	20	27	
Saturday		7	14	21	28	
Sunday	1	8	15	22	29	
Week No.	26	27	28	29	30	31

August					
Monday		6	13	20	27
Tuesday		7	14	21	28
Wednesday	1	8	15	22	29
Thursday	2	9	16	23	30
Friday	3	10	17	24	31
Saturday	4	11	18	25	
Sunday	5	12	19	26	
Week No.	31	32	33	34	35

September					
Monday		3	10	17	24
Tuesday		4	11	18	25
Wednesday		5	12	19	26
Thursday		6	13	20	27
Friday		7	14	21	28
Saturday	1	8	15	22	29
Sunday	2	9	16	23	30
Week No.	35	36	37	38	39

1991

January					
Monday		7	14	21	28
Tuesday	1	8	15	22	29
Wednesday	2	9	16	23	30
Thursday	3	10	17	24	31
Friday	4	11	18	25	
Saturday	5	12	19	26	
Sunday	6	13	20	27	
Week No.	1	2	3	4	5

February					
Monday		4	11	18	25
Tuesday		5	12	19	26
Wednesday		6	13	20	27
Thursday		7	14	21	28
Friday	1	8	15	22	
Saturday	2	9	16	23	
Sunday	3	10	17	24	
Week No.	5	6	7	8	9

March					
Monday		4	11	18	25
Tuesday		5	12	19	26
Wednesday		6	13	20	27
Thursday		7	14	21	28
Friday	1	8	15	22	29
Saturday	2	9	16	23	30
Sunday	3	10	17	24	31
Week No.	9	10	11	12	13

July					
Monday	1	8	15	22	29
Tuesday	2	9	16	23	30
Wednesday	3	10	17	24	31
Thursday	4	11	18	25	
Friday	5	12	19	26	
Saturday	6	13	20	27	
Sunday	7	14	21	28	
Week No.	27	28	29	30	31

August					
Monday		5	12	19	26
Tuesday		6	13	20	27
Wednesday		7	14	21	28
Thursday	1	8	15	22	29
Friday	2	9	16	23	30
Saturday	3	10	17	24	31
Sunday	4	11	18	25	
Week No.	31	32	33	34	35

September						
Monday		2	9	16	23	30
Tuesday		3	10	17	24	
Wednesday		4	11	18	25	
Thursday		5	12	19	26	
Friday		6	13	20	27	
Saturday		7	14	21	28	
Sunday	1	8	15	22	29	
Week No.	35	36	37	38	39	40

1992

January					
Monday		6	13	20	27
Tuesday		7	14	21	28
Wednesday	1	8	15	22	29
Thursday	2	9	16	23	30
Friday	3	10	17	24	31
Saturday	4	11	18	25	
Sunday	5	12	19	26	
Week No.	1	2	3	4	5

February					
Monday		3	10	17	24
Tuesday		4	11	18	25
Wednesday		5	12	19	26
Thursday		6	13	20	27
Friday		7	14	21	28
Saturday	1	8	15	22	29
Sunday	2	9	16	23	
Week No.	5	6	7	8	9

March						
Monday		2	9	16	23	30
Tuesday		3	10	17	24	31
Wednesday		4	11	18	25	
Thursday		5	12	19	26	
Friday		6	13	20	27	
Saturday		7	14	21	28	
Sunday	1	8	15	22	29	
Week No.	9	10	11	12	13	14

July					
Monday		6	13	20	27
Tuesday		7	14	21	28
Wednesday	1	8	15	22	29
Thursday	2	9	16	23	30
Friday	3	10	17	24	31
Saturday	4	11	18	25	
Sunday	5	12	19	26	
Week No.	27	28	29	30	31

August						
Monday		3	10	17	24	31
Tuesday		4	11	18	25	
Wednesday		5	12	19	26	
Thursday		6	13	20	27	
Friday		7	14	21	28	
Saturday	1	8	15	22	29	
Sunday	2	9	16	23	30	
Week No.	31	32	33	34	35	36

September					
Monday		7	14	21	28
Tuesday	1	8	15	22	29
Wednesday	2	9	16	23	30
Thursday	3	10	17	24	
Friday	4	11	18	25	
Saturday	5	12	19	26	
Sunday	6	13	20	27	
Week No.	36	37	38	39	40

Summary Calendar

1990

April						
Monday		2	9	16	23	30
Tuesday		3	10	17	24	
Wednesday		4	11	18	25	
Thursday		5	12	19	26	
Friday		6	13	20	27	
Saturday		7	14	21	28	
Sunday	1	8	15	22	29	
Week No.	13	14	15	16	17	18

May					
Monday		7	14	21	28
Tuesday	1	8	15	22	29
Wednesday	2	9	16	23	30
Thursday	3	10	17	24	31
Friday	4	11	18	25	
Saturday	5	12	19	26	
Sunday	6	13	20	27	
Week No.	18	19	20	21	22

June					
Monday		4	11	18	25
Tuesday		5	12	19	26
Wednesday		6	13	20	27
Thursday		7	14	21	28
Friday	1	8	15	22	29
Saturday	2	9	16	23	30
Sunday	3	10	17	24	
Week No.	22	23	24	25	26

October					
Monday	1	8	15	22	29
Tuesday	2	9	16	23	30
Wednesday	3	10	17	24	31
Thursday	4	11	18	25	
Friday	5	12	19	26	
Saturday	6	13	20	27	
Sunday	7	14	21	28	
Week No.	40	41	42	43	44

November					
Monday		5	12	19	26
Tuesday		6	13	20	27
Wednesday		7	14	21	28
Thursday	1	8	15	22	29
Friday	2	9	16	23	30
Saturday	3	10	17	24	
Sunday	4	11	18	25	
Week No.	44	45	46	47	48

December						
Monday		3	10	17	24	31
Tuesday		4	11	18	25	
Wednesday		5	12	19	26	
Thursday		6	13	20	27	
Friday		7	14	21	28	
Saturday	1	8	15	22	29	
Sunday	2	9	16	23	30	
Week No.	48	49	50	51	52	1

1991

April					
Monday	1	8	15	22	29
Tuesday	2	9	16	23	30
Wednesday	3	10	17	24	
Thursday	4	11	18	25	
Friday	5	12	19	26	
Saturday	6	13	20	27	
Sunday	7	14	21	28	
Week No.	14	15	16	17	18

May					
Monday		6	13	20	27
Tuesday		7	14	21	28
Wednesday	1	8	15	22	29
Thursday	2	9	16	23	30
Friday	3	10	17	24	31
Saturday	4	11	18	25	
Sunday	5	12	19	26	
Week No.	18	19	20	21	22

June					
Monday		3	10	17	24
Tuesday		4	11	18	25
Wednesday		5	12	19	26
Thursday		6	13	20	27
Friday		7	14	21	28
Saturday	1	8	15	22	29
Sunday	2	9	16	23	30
Week No.	22	23	24	25	26

October					
Monday		7	14	21	28
Tuesday	1	8	15	22	29
Wednesday	2	9	16	23	30
Thursday	3	10	17	24	31
Friday	4	11	18	25	
Saturday	5	12	19	26	
Sunday	6	13	20	27	
Week No.	40	41	42	43	44

November					
Monday		4	11	18	25
Tuesday		5	12	19	26
Wednesday		6	13	20	27
Thursday		7	14	21	28
Friday	1	8	15	22	29
Saturday	2	9	16	23	30
Sunday	3	10	17	24	
Week No.	44	45	46	47	48

December						
Monday		2	9	16	23	30
Tuesday		3	10	17	24	31
Wednesday		4	11	18	25	
Thursday		5	12	19	26	
Friday		6	13	20	27	
Saturday		7	14	21	28	
Sunday	1	8	15	22	29	
Week No.	48	49	50	51	52	1

1992

April					
Monday		6	13	20	27
Tuesday		7	14	21	28
Wednesday	1	8	15	22	29
Thursday	2	9	16	23	30
Friday	3	10	17	24	
Saturday	4	11	18	25	
Sunday	5	12	19	26	
Week No.	14	15	16	17	18

May					
Monday		4	11	18	25
Tuesday		5	12	19	26
Wednesday		6	13	20	27
Thursday		7	14	21	28
Friday	1	8	15	22	29
Saturday	2	9	16	23	30
Sunday	3	10	17	24	31
Week No.	18	19	20	21	22

June					
Monday	1	8	15	22	29
Tuesday	2	9	16	23	30
Wednesday	3	10	17	24	
Thursday	4	11	18	25	
Friday	5	12	19	26	
Saturday	6	13	20	27	
Sunday	7	14	21	28	
Week No.	23	24	25	26	27

October					
Monday		5	12	19	26
Tuesday		6	13	20	27
Wednesday		7	14	21	28
Thursday	1	8	15	22	29
Friday	2	9	16	23	30
Saturday	3	10	17	24	31
Sunday	4	11	18	25	
Week No.	40	41	42	43	44

November						
Monday		2	9	16	23	30
Tuesday		3	10	17	24	
Wednesday		4	11	18	25	
Thursday		5	12	19	26	
Friday		6	13	20	27	
Saturday		7	14	21	28	
Sunday	1	8	15	22	29	
Week No.	44	45	46	47	48	49

December					
Monday		7	14	21	28
Tuesday	1	8	15	22	29
Wednesday	2	9	16	23	30
Thursday	3	10	17	24	31
Friday	4	11	18	25	
Saturday	5	12	19	26	
Sunday	6	13	20	27	
Week No.	49	50	51	52	53

Notable Dates

	1991		1992		1993	
New Year's Day (UK) □	January	1	January	1	January	1
New Year Holiday (Republic of Ireland) □	January	1	January	1	January	1
Bank Holiday (Scotland)	January	2	January	2	January	2*, 4
St David's Day (Wales)	March	1	March	1	March	1
St Patrick's Day (Republic of Ireland) □	March	17†, 18	March	17	March	17
Bank Holiday (Northern Ireland)	March	17†, 18	March	17	March	17
Mothering Sunday	March	10	March	29	March	21
Vernal Equinox	March	21	March	20	March	20
Good Friday (UK) □▣	March	29	April	17	April	9
Bank Holiday (Scotland and Republic of Ireland)	March	29	April	17	April	9
Easter Monday (UK and Republic of Ireland) □▣	April	1	April	20	April	12
St George's Day (England)	April	23	April	23	April	23
May Day Holiday (UK) □▣	May	6	May	4	May	3
Bank Holiday (Scotland)	May	6	May	4	May	3
Spring Holiday (UK) □▣	May	27	May	25	May	31
Bank Holiday (Scotland)	May	27	May	25	May	31
Holiday (Republic of Ireland) □	June	3	June	1	June	7
Fathers' Day (UK)	June	16	June	21	June	20
Longest Day	June	21	June	21	June	21
Holiday (Northern Ireland) □	July	12	July	12†, 13	July	12
Bank Holiday (Scotland)	August	5	August	3	August	2
Holiday (Republic of Ireland) □	August	5	August	3	August	2
Late Summer Holiday (UK) □▣	August	26	August	31	August	30
Autumnal Equinox	September	23	September	22	September	23
Holiday (Republic of Ireland) □	October	28	October	26	October	25
St Andrew's Day (Scotland)	November	30	November	30	November	30
Shortest Day	December	22	December	21	December	21
Christmas Day (UK and Republic of Ireland) □	December	25	December	25	December	25*
Boxing Day (UK) □▣	December	26	December	26*	December	26†
St Stephen's Day (Republic of Ireland) □	December	26	December	26*	December	26†, 27
Bank Holiday (Scotland)	December	26	December	26*, 28	December	26†, 27, 28
Holiday (UK, except Scotland)	—		December	28	December	27, 28

□ national holiday in country(ies) named ▣ not Scotland *=Saturday †=Sunday (public holidays only)

National Holidays 1991

Australia	January 1, 26*, 28; March 29, 30*; April 1, 25; December 25, 26
Belgium	January 1; April 1; May 1, 9, 20; July 21†; August 15; November 1, 11; December 25
Canada	January 1; March 29; April 1; May 20; July 1; September 2; October 14; November 11; December 25, 26
Denmark	January 1; March 28, 29; April 1, 26; May 9, 20; June 5; December 25, 26
France	January 1; April 1; May 1, 8, 9, 20; July 14†; August 15; November 1, 11; December 25
Germany (FR)	January 1; March 29; April 1; May 1, 9, 20; June 17; November 20; December 25, 26
Greece	January 1, 6†; February 18; March 25; April 5, 8; May 1, 27; August 15; October 28; December 25, 26
Ireland, Republic of	January 1; March 17†, 18; April 1; June 3; August 5; October 28; December 25, 26
Italy	January 1, 6†; March 31†; April 1, 25; May 1; Jun 2†; August 15; November 1, 3†; December 8†, 25, 26
Japan	January 1, 15; February 11; March 21; April 29; May 3, 4*, 5†, 6; September 15†, 16, 23; October 10; November 3†, 4, 23*; December 23
Luxembourg	January 1; April 1; May 1, 9, 20; June 23†, 24; August 15; November 1; December 25, 26
Netherlands	January 1; April 1; May 9, 20; December 25, 26
Portugal	January 1; February 12; March 29; April 25; May 1, 30; June 10; August 15; October 5*; November 1; December 1†, 8†, 25
Saudi Arabia	c. April 9-21; c. June 14-29
Spain	January 1, 6†; March 19, 28, 29; May 1, 30; July 25; August 15; October 12*; November 1; December 6, 8†, 25
United Kingdom	January 1; March 29; April 1; May 6, 27; August 26; December 25, 26
USA	January 1, 21; February 18; May 27; July 4; September 2; October 14; November 11, 28; December 25

Key: *=Saturday †=Sunday

Weights and Measures

Metric Measures and Equivalents

Length

1 millimetre (mm)		=0·0394 in
1 centimetre (cm)	=10 mm	=0·3937 in
1 metre	=100 cm	=1·0936 yd
1 kilometre (km)	=1,000 m	=0·6214 mile

Area

1 sq cm (cm^2)	=100 mm^2	=0·1550 in^2
1 sq metre (m^2)	=10,000 cm^2	=1·1960 yd^2
1 sq km (km^2)	=100 hectares	=0·3861 mile^2

Volume/Capacity

1 cu cm (cm^3)		=0·0610 in^3
1 cu decimetre (dm^3)	=1,000 cm^3	=0·0353 ft^3
1 cu metre (m^3)	=1,000 dm^3	=1·3080 yd^3
1 litre (l)	=1 dm^3	=1·76 pt
		=2·113 US l pt
1 hectolitre (hl)	=100 l	=21·997 gal
		=26·417 US gal

Mass (Weight)

1 milligram (mg)		=0·0154 grain
1 gram (g)	=1,000 mg	=0·0353 oz
1 metric carat	=0·2 g	=3·0865 grains
1 kilogram (kg)	=1,000 g	=2·2046 lb
1 tonne (t)	=1,000 kg	=0·9842 ton
		=1·1023 short ton

Imperial Measures and Equivalents

Length

1 inch (in)		=2·54 cm
1 foot (ft)	=12 in	=0·3048 m
1 yard (yd)	=3 ft	=0·9144 m
1 mile	=1,760 yd	=1·6093 km
1 int nautical mile	=2,025·4 yd	=1·852 km

Area

1 sq inch (in^2)		=6·4516 cm^2
1 sq foot (ft^2)	=144 in^2	=0·0929 m^2
1 sq yard (yd^2)	=9 ft^2	=0·8361 m^2
1 acre	=4,840 yd^2	=4046·9 m^2
1 sq mile (mile^2)	=640 acres	=2·590 km^2

Volume/Capacity

1 cu inch (in^3)		=16·387 cm^3
1 cu foot (ft^3)	=1,728 in^3	=0·0283 m^3
1 cu yard (yd^3)	=27 ft^3	=0·7646 m^3
1 fluid ounce (fl oz)		=28·413 ml
1 pint (pt)	=20 fl oz	=0·5683 l
1 gallon (gal)	=8 pt	=4·546 l

Mass (Weight)

1 ounce (oz)	=437·5 grains	=28·35 g
1 pound (lb)	=16 oz	=0·4536 kg
1 stone	=14 lb	=6·3503 kg
1 hundredweight (cwt)	=112 lb	=50·802 kg
1 ton	=20 cwt	=1·016 t

USA Measures and Equivalents

The definitions for the international pound and yard adopted in 1959 bring USA weights and measures into correspondence with those of the UK, with the exception of the USA measurements of capacity, which include both dry and liquid pints and quarts, the dry derived from the bushel (64 dry pints=1 bushel) and the liquid from the gallon (8 liquid pints=1 US gallon).

The short ton of 2000 lb and the short hundredweight of 100 lb are used more commonly in the USA than in the UK.

USA Dry Measure Equivalents

1 pint	=0·9689 UK pt	=0·5506 l
1 bushel	=1·2445 ft^3	=35·239 l

USA Liquid Measure Equivalents

1 fluid ounce	=1·0408 UK fl oz	=29·574 ml
1 pint (16 fl oz)	=0·8327 UK pt	=0·4732 l
1 gallon	=0·8327 UK gal	=3·7854 l

Temperature Conversion

Celsius: −18° −10 0 10 20 30 40 50 60 70 80 90 100°

Fahrenheit: 0° 10 20 32 40 50 60 70 80 90 100 110 120 130 140 150 160 170 180 190 200 212°

$C = \frac{5}{9}(F-32)$ $F = \frac{9}{5}C+32$

Conversion Tables

LENGTH

centimetres (cm)	cm or inches	inches (in)
2·54	**1**	0·394
5·08	**2**	0·787
7·62	**3**	1·181
10·16	**4**	1·575
12·70	**5**	1·969
15·24	**6**	2·362
17·78	**7**	2·756
20·32	**8**	3·150
22·86	**9**	3·543
25·40	**10**	3·937
50·80	**20**	7·874
76·20	**30**	11·811
101·60	**40**	15·748
127·00	**50**	19·685
152·40	**60**	23·622
177·80	**70**	27·559
203·20	**80**	31·496
228·60	**90**	35·433
254·00	**100**	39·370

kilometres (km)	km or miles	miles
1·609	**1**	0·621
3·219	**2**	1·243
4·828	**3**	1·864
6·437	**4**	2·485
8·047	**5**	3·107
9·656	**6**	3·728
11·265	**7**	4·350
12·875	**8**	4·971
14·484	**9**	5·592
16·093	**10**	6·214
32·187	**20**	12·427
48·280	**30**	18·641
64·374	**40**	24·855
80·467	**50**	31·069
96·561	**60**	37·282
112·654	**70**	43·496
128·748	**80**	49·710
144·841	**90**	55·923
160·934	**100**	62·137

MASS (WEIGHT)

kilograms (kg)	kg or lb	pounds (lb)
0·454	**1**	2·205
0·907	**2**	4·409
1·361	**3**	6·614
1·814	**4**	8·819
2·268	**5**	11·023
2·722	**6**	13·228
3·175	**7**	15·432
3·629	**8**	17·637
4·082	**9**	19·842
4·536	**10**	22·046
9·072	**20**	44·092
13·608	**30**	66·139
18·144	**40**	88·185
22·680	**50**	110·231
27·216	**60**	132·277
31·752	**70**	154·324
36·287	**80**	176·370
40·823	**90**	198·416
45·359	**100**	220·462

tonnes (t)	t or UK tons	UK tons
1·016	**1**	0·984
2·032	**2**	1·968
3·048	**3**	2·953
4·064	**4**	3·937
5·080	**5**	4·921
6·096	**6**	5·905
7·112	**7**	6·889
8·128	**8**	7·874
9·144	**9**	8·858
10·161	**10**	9·842
20·321	**20**	19·684
30·481	**30**	29·526
40·642	**40**	39·368
50·802	**50**	49·210
60·963	**60**	59·052
71·123	**70**	68·894
81·284	**80**	78·737
91·444	**90**	88·579
101·605	**100**	98·421

AREA

hectares (ha)	ha or acres	acres
0·405	**1**	2·471
0·809	**2**	4·942
1·214	**3**	7·413
1·619	**4**	9·884
2·023	**5**	12·355
2·428	**6**	14·826
2·833	**7**	17·297
3·237	**8**	19·769
3·642	**9**	22·240
4·047	**10**	24·711
8·094	**20**	49·421
12·140	**30**	74·132
16·187	**40**	98·842
20·234	**50**	123·553
24·281	**60**	148·263
28·328	**70**	172·974
32·375	**80**	197·684
36·422	**90**	222·395
40·469	**100**	247·105

VOLUME

litres	litres or UK gallons	UK gallons
4·546	**1**	0·220
9·092	**2**	0·440
13·638	**3**	0·660
18·184	**4**	0·880
22·730	**5**	1·100
27·276	**6**	1·320
31·822	**7**	1·540
36·368	**8**	1·760
40·914	**9**	1·980
45·460	**10**	2·200
90·919	**20**	4·399
136·379	**30**	6·599
181·839	**40**	8·799
227·298	**50**	10·998
272·758	**60**	13·198
318·217	**70**	15·398
363·677	**80**	17·598
409·137	**90**	19·797
454·596	**100**	21·997

World Time Zones

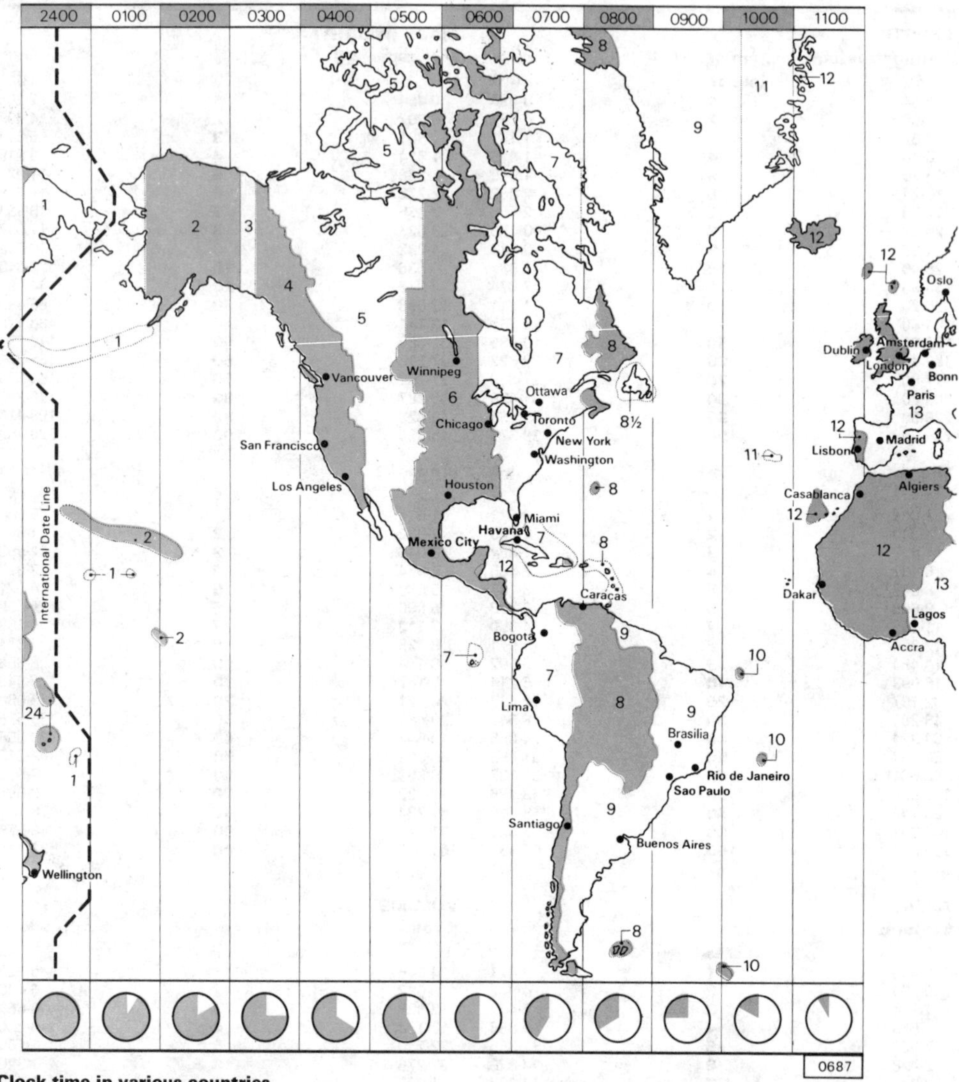

Clock time in various countries

	At noon GMT Standard time	Daylight Saving	
Australia:			
South Australia	2130	2230	Late Oct–late March
New South Wales	2200	2300	
Tasmania	2200	2300	
Victoria	2200	2300	
Austria	1300	1400	Late Mar–late Sep
Belgium	1300	1400	Late Mar–late Sep
Bulgaria	1400	1500	Apr–late Sep
Canada:			
Newfoundland	0830	0930	Early Apr–Oct
Atlantic	0800	0900	
Eastern	0700	0800	

	At noon GMT Standard time	Daylight Saving	
Canada:			
Central	0600	0700	Early Apr–Oct
Mountain	0500	0600	
Pacific	0400	0500	
Yukon	0400	0500	
Czechoslovakia	1300	1400	Late Mar–late Sep
Denmark	1300	1400	Late Mar–late Sep
Egypt	1400	1500	June–Sep
Finland	1400	1500	Late Mar–late Sep
France	1300	1400	Late Mar–late Sep
Germany (East)	1300	1400	Late Mar–late Sep
Germany (West)	1300	1400	Late Mar–late Sep

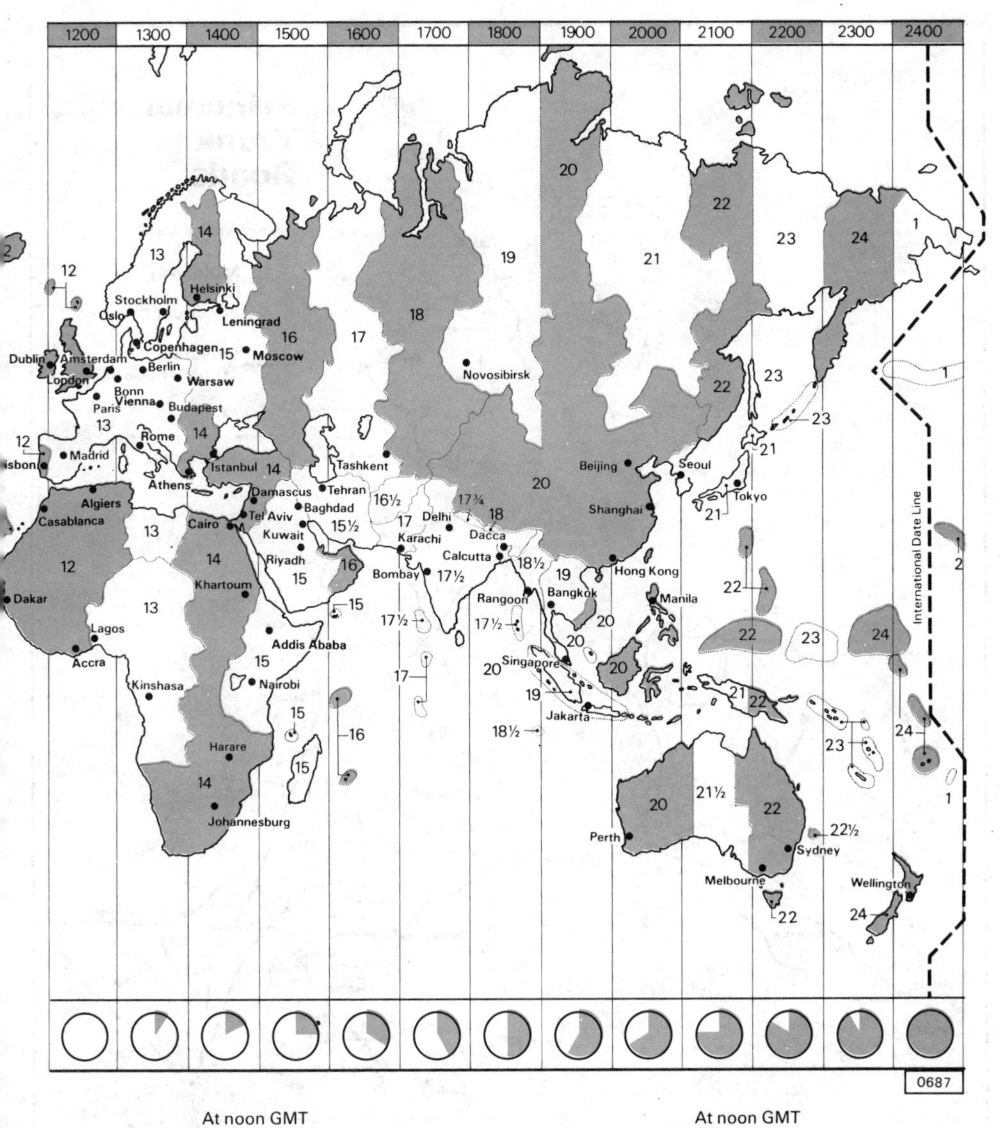

	At noon GMT Standard time	Daylight Saving	
Greece	1400	1500	Late Mar – late Sep
Hungary	1300	1400	Late Mar – late Sep
Iraq	1500	1600	Late Mar – late Sep
Ireland	1200	1300	Late Mar – late Oct
Italy	1300	1400	Late Mar – late Sep
Luxembourg	1300	1400	Late Mar – late Sep
Netherlands	1300	1400	Late Mar – late Sep
New Zealand	2400	0100	Late Oct – early Mar
Norway	1300	1400	Late Mar – late Sep
Poland	1300	1400	Late Mar – late Sep
Portugal	1200	1300	Late Mar – late Sep
Spain	1300	1400	Late Mar – late Sep

	At noon GMT Standard time	Daylight Saving	
Sweden	1300	1400	Late Mar – late Sep
Switzerland	1300	1400	Late Mar – late Sep
United Kingdom	1200	1300	Late Mar – late Oct
United States:			
Eastern	0700	0800	Early Apr – Oct
Central	0600	0700	
Mountain	0500	0600	
Pacific	0400	0500	
USSR			
Kiev, Moscow	1500	1600	Apr – Sep
Novosibirsk	1900	2000	
Vladivostok	2200	2300	

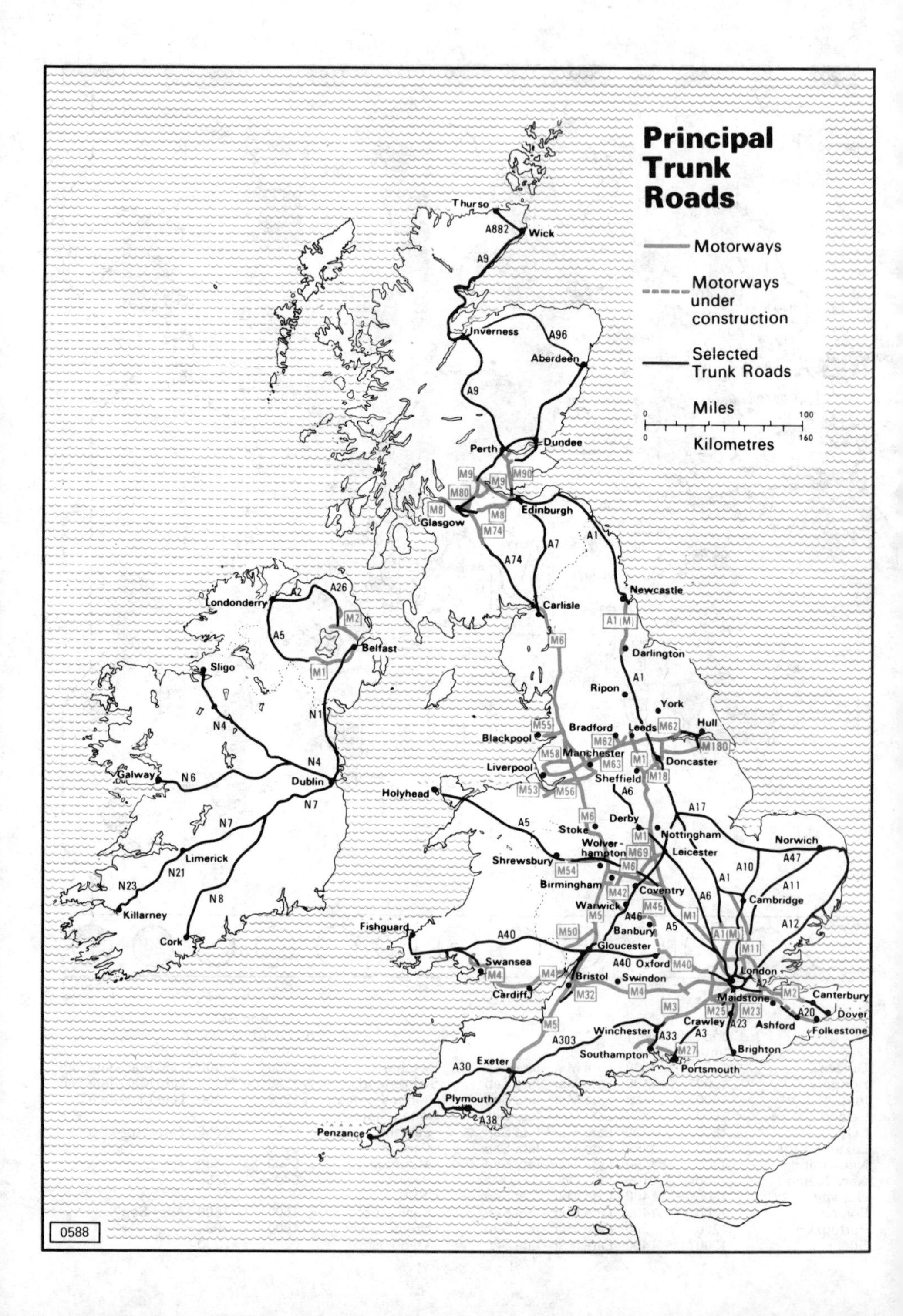
Principal Trunk Roads
Motorways
Motorways under construction
Selected Trunk Roads
Miles
0
100
0
160
Kilometres
Thurso
Wick
A882
A9
Inverness
A96
Aberdeen
A9
Perth
Dundee
M9
M9
M90
M80
M8
M8
Edinburgh
Glasgow
M74
A7
A1
A74
Londonderry
A2
A26
M2
A5
Belfast
M1
Carlisle
Newcastle
A1(M)
M6
Darlington
A1
Ripon
York
Sligo
N1
N4
N4
Galway
N6
Dublin
N7
N7
Limerick
N21
N23
Killarney
N8
Cork
Holyhead
A5
M55
Blackpool
Bradford
Leeds
M62
Hull
M62
Manchester
M180
M58
M1
Doncaster
Liverpool
M63
Sheffield
M18
M53
M56
A6
A17
M6
Stoke
Derby
M1
Nottingham
Norwich
Shrewsbury
Wolverhampton
M69
Leicester
A47
M54
M6
A10
Birmingham
A1
A11
M42
Coventry
A6
Cambridge
Warwick
M45
M1
A12
A46
M5
Banbury
A5
A1(M)
Fishguard
A40
M50
Gloucester
M11
Swansea
A40
Oxford
M40
London
M4
M4
Bristol
Swindon
A2
M2
Canterbury
Cardiff
M32
M4
Maidstone
A20
Dover
M3
M25
M23
Ashford
Folkestone
M5
Crawley
Winchester
A33
A3
A23
A303
M27
Brighton
Southampton
Portsmouth
A30
Exeter
Plymouth
A38
Penzance
0588

Road Distances (miles and kilometres)

Distance based on AA Recommended routes. Miles in roman type kilometres in *italic* type.	Aberdeen	Birmingham	Brighton	Bristol	Cardiff	Carlisle	Dover	Edinburgh	Fort William	Glasgow	Holyhead	Hull	Inverness	Leeds	Liverpool	London	Manchester	Newcastle	Norwich	Nottingham	Penzance	Plymouth	Sheffield
Aberdeen	—	*692*	*983*	*827*	*859*	*373*	*1014*	*203*	*256*	*235*	*743*	*578*	*171*	*557*	*575*	*879*	*566*	*380*	*817*	*666*	*1133*	*1012*	*623*
Birmingham	430	—	*298*	*142*	*174*	*319*	*330*	*480*	*655*	*478*	*245*	*219*	*734*	*187*	*163*	*193*	*143*	*327*	*262*	*87*	*447*	*327*	*140*
Brighton	611	185	—	*267*	*323*	*608*	*126*	*769*	*946*	*778*	*536*	*455*	*1024*	*425*	*452*	*97*	*433*	*563*	*270*	*315*	*462*	*341*	*377*
Bristol	514	88	166	—	*76*	*477*	*332*	*613*	*790*	*613*	*380*	*372*	*869*	*354*	*298*	*193*	*277*	*480*	*375*	*237*	*322*	*201*	*293*
Cardiff	534	108	201	47	—	*486*	*388*	*645*	*822*	*645*	*330*	*404*	*901*	*386*	*330*	*249*	*309*	*511*	*431*	*269*	*381*	*261*	*325*
Carlisle	232	198	378	282	302	—	*641*	*159*	*336*	*159*	*370*	*278*	*415*	*198*	*201*	*504*	*192*	*917*	*459*	*306*	*760*	*639*	*269*
Dover	630	205	78	206	241	398	—	*747*	*977*	*800*	*566*	*426*	*1056*	*435*	*484*	*127*	*465*	*565*	*272*	*348*	*591*	*470*	*409*
Edinburgh	126	298	478	381	401	99	464	—	*214*	*76*	*531*	*370*	*253*	*332*	*362*	*665*	*352*	*172*	*592*	*439*	*919*	*798*	*396*
Fort William	159	407	588	491	511	209	607	133	—	*166*	*706*	*615*	*105*	*536*	*538*	*842*	*529*	*391*	*797*	*644*	*1096*	*975*	*607*
Glasgow	146	297	477	381	401	99	497	47	103	—	*529*	*438*	*277*	*57*	*360*	*663*	*351*	*245*	*618*	*467*	*919*	*798*	*428*
Holyhead	462	152	333	236	205	230	352	330	439	329	—	*359*	*785*	*270*	*169*	*431*	*201*	*431*	*480*	*283*	*686*	*565*	*254*
Hull	359	136	283	231	251	173	265	230	382	272	223	—	*694*	*98*	*209*	*351*	*159*	*229*	*245*	*150*	*678*	*557*	*108*
Inverness	106	456	636	540	560	258	656	157	65	172	488	431	—	*615*	*616*	*919*	*608*	*431*	*874*	*723*	*1175*	*1054*	*684*
Leeds	346	116	264	220	240	123	270	206	333	222	168	61	382	—	*121*	*320*	*71*	*150*	*278*	*117*	*700*	*539*	*66*
Liverpool	357	101	281	185	205	125	301	225	334	224	105	130	383	75	—	*348*	*56*	*282*	*389*	*175*	*603*	*483*	*124*
London	546	120	60	120	155	313	79	413	523	412	268	218	571	199	216	—	*328*	*459*	*185*	*211*	*509*	*388*	*272*
Manchester	352	89	269	172	192	119	289	219	329	218	125	99	378	44	35	204	—	*232*	*306*	*114*	*583*	*462*	*60*
Newcastle	236	203	350	298	318	57	351	107	243	152	268	142	268	93	175	285	144	—	*410*	*257*	*785*	*665*	*216*
Norwich	508	163	168	233	268	285	169	368	495	384	298	152	543	173	242	115	190	255	—	*192*	*685*	*570*	*252*
Nottingham	414	54	196	147	167	190	216	273	400	290	176	93	449	73	109	131	71	160	119	—	*542*	*422*	*71*
Penzance	704	278	287	200	237	472	367	571	681	571	426	421	730	410	375	316	362	488	426	337	—	*122*	*599*
Plymouth	629	203	212	125	162	397	292	496	606	496	351	346	655	335	300	241	287	413	354	262	78	—	*478*
Sheffield	387	87	234	182	202	167	254	246	377	266	158	67	425	41	77	169	37	134	149	44	364	297	—

Airports

Aberdeen
Dyce, Aberdeen 0224 722331

Alderney
Alderney, C.I. 048 182 2886

Belfast
Aldergrove, Belfast BT29 4AB 0232 457745

Birmingham
Birmingham B26 3QJ 021-767 5511

Blackpool
Blackpool FY4 2QY 0253 43061

Bournemouth
Christchurch, Dorset BH23 6DB 0202 579751

Bristol
Lulsgate, Bristol BS19 3DY 027 587 4441

Cambridge
Newmarket Road, Cambridge CB5 8RX 0223 61133

Cardiff-Wales
Rhoose, Cardiff CF6 9BD 0446 711111

Coventry
Baginton, Coventry CV8 3AZ 0203 301717

Dundee
Riverside Drive, Dundee 0382 643242

East Midlands
Castle Donington, Derby DE7 2SA 0332 810621

Edinburgh
Edinburgh EH12 9DN 031-333 1000

Exeter
Exeter EX5 2BD 0392 67433

Glasgow
Paisley, Renfrewshire 041-887 1111

Gloucester and Cheltenham
Staverton, nr. Cheltenham, Glos. GL51 6SR 0452 713095

Guernsey (States)
Villiaze Forest, Guernsey contact indiv. airlines

Humberside
Kirmington, South Humberside DN39 6YH 0652 688456

Isle of Man
Ballasalla, Isle of Man 0624 823311

Jersey (States)
St Peter, Jersey, C.I. 0534 46111

Leeds and Bradford
Yeadon, nr. Leeds 0532 509696

Liverpool
Speke, Liverpool L24 1YD 051-486 8877

London-City
London E16 2PX 071-474 5555

London-Gatwick
Gatwick, West Sussex RH6 0NP 0293 28822

London-Heathrow
Hounslow, Middlesex TW6 1JH 01-759 4321

London-Stansted
Stansted, Essex CM24 8QW 0279 502380

Luton
Luton, Bedfordshire LU2 9LY 0582 405100

Lydd
Romney Marsh, Kent PN29 9QL 0679 20401

Manchester
Wythenshawe, Manchester M22 5PA 061-489 3000

Newcastle
Woolsington, Newcastle-upon-Tyne NE13 8BZ 091-286 0966

Norwich
Cromer Road, Norwich NR6 6JA 0603 411923

Plymouth
Crownhill, Plymouth PL6 8BW 0752 707023

Prestwick
Prestwick, Ayrshire KA9 2PL 0292 79822

RAF Biggin Hill
Kent TN16 3BN 0959 71111

RAF Manston
Nr Ramsgate, Kent CT12 5BS 0843 823351

Shoreham
Shoreham-by-Sea, Sussex BN4 5FJ 0273 452304

Southampton
Southampton SO9 1RH 0703 629600

Southend
Southend-on-Sea SS2 6YF 0702 340201

Sumburgh
Virkie, Shetland Isles ZE3 9JP 0950 60654

Teesside
Darlington, Co. Durham DL2 1LU 0325 332811

AIR TRAVEL

Air London (Aircraft charter)
Mack House, Aviation Court,
Gatwick Road, Crawley,
West Sussex RH10 2GG 0293 549555

British Airports Services Ltd
Masefield House, Gatwick,
West Sussex RH6 0HZ 0293 517755

British Airways
Reservations TBC,
1st Floor, Hatton Cross,
Hounslow, Middlesex TW6 2JA 081-897 4000

British Midland Airways
Donington Hall,
Castle Donington, Derby DE7 2SB 0332 810552

Dan-Air Services
Newman House, Victoria Road,
Horley, Surrey 0345 100 200

Wardair (UK)
1st and 2nd Floor, Rothschild House,
Whitgift Centre, Croydon,
Surrey CR9 3HN 0800 234444

Cabair Air Taxis (Helicopter and aircraft charter)
Elstree Aerodrome,
Boreham Wood,
Hertfordshire WD6 3AW 081-953 4411

Overseas Air Line Offices in London

Aer Lingus
83 Staines Road, Hounslow, Middlesex TW3 3JB 081-569 5555

Aeroflot
70 Piccadilly, W1 071-493 7436

Air Afrique
177 Piccadilly, W1 071-493 4881

Air Algérie
10 Baker Street, W1 071-487 5903

Air Canada
7/8 Conduit Street, W1 071-439 7941

Air Europe
The Galleria, Station Road, Crawley 0293 562626

Air France
158 New Bond Street, W1 071-499 9511

Air India
17/18 New Bond Street, W1 071-491 7979

Air Jamaica
5th Floor, Sabena House, 36 Piccadilly 071-734 1782

Air Lanka
6/10 Bruton Street, W1 071-439 0291

Air Malta
23 Pall Mall, SW1 071-839 5872

Air New Zealand
Haymarket, SW1 071-930 3434

Air Portugal
19 Regent Street, W1 071-828 0262

Alia, The Royal Jordanian Airlines,
177 Regent Street, W1 071-734 2557

Alitalia
205 Holland Park Avenue 071-602 7111

Cathay Pacific
52 Berkeley Street, W1 071-930 7878

Egyptair
29-31 Piccadilly, W1 071-580 4239

El Al Israel
185 Regent Street, W1 071-437 9255

Gulf Air
10 Albemarle Street, W1 071-408 1717

Iberia
130 Regent Street, W1 071-437 5622

Iraqi Airways
4 Regent Street, W1 071-930 1155

Japan Air
Hanover Court, 5 Hanover Square, W1 071-408 1000

KLM
8 Hanover Street, W1 081-568 9144

Kuwait Airways
16 Baker Street, W1 071-935 8795

Lufthansa
23/26 Piccadilly, W1 071-408 0322

Olympic Airways
164 Piccadilly, W1 081-846 9080

Pakistan International
45/46 Piccadilly, W1 071-734 5544

Pan American
193 Piccadilly, W1 071-409 0688

Qantas
169 Regent Street, W1 081-846 0466

Sabena
36 Piccadilly, W1 071-437 6950

SAS
52 Conduit Street, W1 071-734 4020

Singapore Airlines
143 Regent Street, W1 071-439 8111

South African Airways
251/259 Regent Street, W1 071-734 9841

Swissair
10 Wardour Street, W1 071-439 4144

Syrian Arab Airlines
27 Albemarle Street, W1 071-493 2851

TWA
200 Piccadilly, W1 071-439 0707

Varig (Brazil)
16 Hanover Street, W1 071-629 5824

Yugoslav
37 Maddox Street, W1 071-493 9399

A few Travel Hints
The latest time you should arrive at the airport is one hour before take-off and the big airports recommend that you should check-in two hours before take-off. When travelling by scheduled flight you should ask your hotel to re-confirm your departure time as soon as possible after arrival.

USEFUL PHONE NUMBERS

Credit Card Companies

Access, Southend-on-Sea	0702 352211
American Express	071-930 4411
Barclaycard, Northampton	0604 234234
Carte Blanche, Farnborough, Hants	0252 515809
Diners Club, Farnborough, Hants	0252 516261
TSB Trustcard, Brighton	0273 724666

British Rail

Enquiries – King's Cross	071-278 2477
London Midland Region	071-387 7070
Network South East	071-928 5100
Western Region	071-262 6767
Scottish region	041-204 2844
Continental Enquiries	071-834 2345
Birmingham	021-643 2711
Bournemouth	0202 292474
Brighton	0273-206755
Bristol	0272 294255
Cardiff	0222 228000
Dover	0227 454411
Edinburgh	031-556 2451
Glasgow	041-204 2844
Leeds	0532 448133
Liverpool	051-709 9696
Manchester	061-832 8353
Newcastle	091-232 6262
Norwich	0603 632055
Plymouth	0752 221300
Sheffield	0742 726411
York	0904 642155

Religious Festivals and Anniversaries

	1991		1992	
Christian—Western				
Ash Wednesday	February	13	March	4
Quadragesima	February	17	March	8
Palm Sunday	March	24	April	12
Good Friday	March	29	April	17
Easter Day	March	31	April	19
Ascension Day	May	9	May	28
Whit Sunday	May	19	June	7
Trinity Sunday	June	2	June	14
Advent Sunday	December	1	November	29
Christmas Day	December	25	December	25
Roman Catholic—Holidays of Obligation				
Solemnity of Our Lady (Scotland)	January	1	January	1
Epiphany (not Ireland)	January	6	January	6
St Patrick (Ireland)	March	17	March	17
St Joseph (Scotland)	March	19	March	19
Ascension	May	9	May	28
Corpus Christi	May	30	June	18
St Peter and St Paul (not Ireland)	June	29	June	29
Assumption	August	15	August	15*
All Saints	November	1	November	1†
Immaculate Conception (Scotland and Ireland)	December	8	December	8
Christmas	December	25	December	25
Christian—Eastern Orthodox				
Lent Monday	February	18	March	9
Easter Day	April	7	April	26
Pentecost	May	26	June	14
Chinese				
Lunar New Year (3 days)	February	15-17	February	4-6
Hindu				
Janmashtami	September	2	August	21
Diwali	November	5	October	25
Islamic*	**A.H. 1411**		**A.H. 1412**	
Lailat Al-Isra wa Al-Miraj	February	10	January	31
Lailat Bara'ah	February	28	February	17
1st of Ramadan	March	17	March	5
Eid-Al-Fittr	April	15	April	4
Eid-Al-Addha	June	22	June	11
	A.H. 1412		**A.H. 1413**	
Al Hijra (Islamic New Year)	July	12	–	
Ashura	July	21	–	
Milad al-Nabi (Prophet's Birthday)	September	20	–	
*Islamic dates are subject to visibility of new moon at Mecca				
Jewish	**5751**		**5752**	
Purim	February	28	March	19
Pessach (Passover) 1st Day	March	30*	April	18*
Shavuot (Pentecost) 1st Day	May	19	June	7
Fast of 17th Tammuz	June	30‡	July	19‡
Fast of 9th Ab	July	21‡	August	9‡
‡ Observed on Sunday as actual festival day is a Sabbath				
	5752		**5753**	
Rosh Hashanah (Jewish New Year)	September	9	September	28
Yom Kippur (Day of Atonement)	September	18	October	7
Chanucah 1st Day	December	2	December	20
Sikh				
Birthday of Guru Gobind Singh Ji	–		January	12
			December	31
Baisakhi	April	14	April	13
Martyrdom of Guru Arjan Dev Ji	June	15	June	4
Birthday of Guru Nanak Dev Ji	November	21	November	10

1991 Exhibitions

JANUARY

Retirement
National Exhibition Centre
(Birmingham) 3-6 June

London International Boat Show
Earls Court
3-13 January

Holiday and Travel Fair
National Exhibition Centre
(Birmingham) 3-6 January

FEBRUARY

Crufts—Centenary Year
National Exhibition Centre
9-12 February

MAPS—Marketing Exhibition
National Exhibition Centre
19-21 February

MARCH

Daily Mail Ideal Home Exhibition
Earls Court
Tel: 071 222 9341

Norex
Park Avenue Hotel, Belfast
4-9 March

Scothot
Scottish Exhibition and Conference Centre, Glasgow
17-21 March

APRIL

Expoship 91
Barbican Exhibition Halls
Tel: 071-588 8211

British International Antiques Fair
National Exhibition Centre
4-10 April

MAY

Chelsea Flower Show
Royal Hospital, Chelsea
Tel: 071-834 4333

Interior Design International
Earls Court
12-16 May

Shopex International
Earls Court
12-16 May

RoSpa International Safety and Health Exhibition
National Exhibition Centre
21-23 May

JUNE

Solicitor's Show
Barbican Exhibition Halls
Tel: 071-588 8211

Computers in Personnel
Barbican Exhibition Halls
Tel: 071-588 8211

Royal International Horse Show & Fair
National Exhibition Centre
13-17 June

Royal Highland Agricultural Show
Ingliston, Edinburgh
16-19 June

JULY

Royal Agricultural Show
Kenilworth, Coventry
Tel: Coventry 696969

Royal Welsh Show
Builth Wells, Powys
22-25 July

AUGUST

NEC August Fair
National Exhibition Centre
8-11 August

Norex
Park Avenue Hotel, Belfast
26-31 August

SEPTEMBER

International Police Exhibition and Conference
Barbican Exhibition Halls
Tel: 071-588 8211

City of London Wine Fair
Tel: 071-588 8211

OCTOBER

London Motor Fair
Earls Court Tel: 071 370 8223

London Printing Equipment Show
Barbican Exhibition Halls
Tel: 071 588 8211

Aerotech
National Exhibition Centre
29 Oct-1 Nov

NOVEMBER

International Motor Cycle Exhibition
Earls Court
Tel: Coventry 27427

Computers in the City
Barbican Exhibition Halls
Tel: 071-588 8211

Accountants Exhibition
Barbican Exhibition Halls
Tel: 071 588 8211

City of London Antiques Fair
Barbican Exhibition Halls
Tel: 071-588 8211

Lease
National Exhibition Centre
5-7 November

Autotech
National Exhibition Centre
12-15 November

Royal Welsh Agricultural Winter Fair
Builth Wells, Powys
26 November

You are advised to contact the venue direct to confirm that the event is taking place and if events are Trade only. When firm dates are not available a contact phone number is given.

Frequently used Telephone Numbers

Personal Notes

British Summer Time: At time of going to press, the Home Office was unable to confirm the 1991 starting and finishing dates for British Summer Time. **(Accordingly all sunrise and sunset times have been expressed as GMT**. When dates are confirmed **add one hour to give these times as BST.)**

Scottish Bank Holidays The term 'Bank Holiday' has a restricted meaning in Scotland, where it does not necessarily signify a national public holiday. For this reason, Scottish bank holidays are differentiated in this diary from public holidays in the rest of the United Kingdom, with the exception of Christmas Day and New Year's Day, which are generally accepted as national holidays in Scotland.

Week Numbering The system of week numbering followed in this diary is that recommended by the International Organization for Standardization (ISO), according to which Week 1 is the first week containing four or more days of the new year. Monday is taken as the first day of the week.

The Astronomical Information in this diary is reproduced, with permission, from data supplied by the Science and Engineering Research Council. Sunrise and Sunset times are based on London. The information given is correct at the time of going to press. The calendar notes refer to Great Britain.

E&OE

Monday 31
365–0 Week 1

Tuesday January 1991 1
1–364 Week 1
New Year's Day Holiday (UK)
Holiday (Republic of Ireland) Holiday (Australia)

Wednesday 2
2–363 Week 1
Bank Holiday (Scotland)

Thursday **3**
3–362 Week 1

Friday **4**
4–361 Week 1 PAYE Week 40

Saturday **5**
5–360 Week 1
sr 8.06, ss 16.06

Sunday **6**
6–359 Week 1
Epiphany

Monday **7**

7–358 Week 2

☾ Last Quarter

Tuesday **8**

8–357 Week 2

Wednesday **9**

9–356 Week 2

Thursday **10**
10–355 Week 2

Friday **11**
11–354 Week 2 PAYE week 41

Saturday **12**
12–353 Week 2
sr 8.02, ss 16.16

Sunday **13**
13–352 Week 2
1st after Epiphany

Monday **14**
14–351 Week 3

Tuesday **15**
15–350 Week 3
● New Moon

Wednesday **16**
16–349 Week 3

Thursday **17**
17–348 Week 3

Friday **18**
18–347 Week 3 PAYE week 42

Saturday **19**
19–346 Week 3
sr 7.56, ss 16.27

Sunday **20**
20–345 Week 3
2nd after Epiphany

Monday **21**
21–344 Week 4

Tuesday **22**
22–343 Week 4

Wednesday **23**
23–342 Week 4
☽ First Quarter

Thursday **24**
24–341 Week 4

Friday **25**
25–340 Week 4 PAYE week 43

Saturday **26**
26–339 Week 4
Australia Day sr 7.48, ss 16.39

Sunday **27**
27–338 Week 4
Septuagesima

1991 January

Monday 28
28–337 Week 5
Holiday (Australia)

Tuesday 29
29–336 Week 5

Wednesday 30
30–335 Week 5
○ Full Moon

Thursday **31**
31–334 Week 5

Friday **February** **1**
32–333 Week 5 PAYE week 44

Saturday **2**
33–332 Week 5
Candlemas (Scottish Quarter Day) sr 7.38, ss 16.51

Sunday **3**
34–331 Week 5
Sexagesima

Monday **4**
35–330 Week 6

Tuesday **5**
36–329 Week 6

Wednesday **6**
37–328 Week 6
☾ Last Quarter

Thursday **7**
38–327 Week 6

Friday **8**
39–326 Week 6 PAYE week 45

Saturday **9**
40–325 Week 6
sr 7.27, ss 17.04

Sunday **10**
41–324 Week 6
Quinquagesima

Monday **11**
42–323 Week 7

Tuesday **12**
43–322 Week 7
Shrove Tuesday

Wednesday **13**
44–321 Week 7
Ash Wednesday

Thursday 14
45–320 Week 7
St Valentine
● New Moon

Friday 15
46–319 Week 7 PAYE week 46

Saturday 16
47–318 Week 7
sr 7.14, ss 17.17

Sunday 17
48–317 Week 7
Quadragesima (1st in Lent)

Monday **18**
49–316 Week 8

Tuesday **19**
50–315 Week 8

Wednesday **20**
51–314 Week 8

Thursday **21**
52–313 Week 8
☽ First Quarter

Friday **22**
53–312 Week 8 PAYE week 47

Saturday **23**
54–311 Week 8
sr 7.00, ss 17.29

Sunday **24**
55–310 Week 8
2nd in Lent

Monday 25
56–309 Week 9

Tuesday 26
57–308 Week 9

Wednesday 27
58–307 Week 9

Thursday **28**
59–306 Week 9
○ Full Moon

Friday March **1**
60–305 Week 9 PAYE week 48
St David (Wales)

Saturday **2**
61–304 Week 9
sr 6.45, ss 17.42

Sunday **3**
62–303 Week 9
3rd in Lent

Monday **4**
63–302 Week 10

Tuesday **5**
64–301 Week 10

Wednesday **6**
65–300 Week 10

Thursday **7**
66–299 Week 10

Friday **8**
67–298 Week 10 PAYE week 49
☾ Last Quarter

Saturday **9**
68–297 Week 10
sr 6.30, ss 17.54

Sunday **10**
69–296 Week 10
4th in Lent Mothering Sunday

Monday **11**
70–295 Week 11

Tuesday **12**
71–294 Week 11

Wednesday **13**
72–293 Week 11

Thursday **14**
73–292 Week 11

Friday **15**
74–291 Week 11 PAYE week 50

Saturday **16**
75–290 Week 11
sr 6.14, ss 18.06 ● New Moon

Sunday **17**
76–289 Week 11
Passion Sunday St Patrick (Ireland)

Monday **18**

77–288 Week 12

Holiday (Republic of Ireland)

Bank Holiday (Northern Ireland)

Tuesday **19**

78–287 Week 12

Wednesday **20**

79–286 Week 12

Thursday **21**
80–285 Week 12
Vernal Equinox

Friday **22**
81–284 Week 12 PAYE week 51

Saturday **23**
82–283 Week 12
sr 5.58, ss 18.18 ☽ First Quarter

Sunday **24**
83–282 Week 12
Palm Sunday

Monday **25**
84–281 Week 13
Lady Day (Quarter Day)

Tuesday **26**
85–280 Week 13

Wednesday **27**
86–279 Week 13

Thursday 28
87–278 Week 13
Maundy Thursday

Friday 29
88–277 Week 13 PAYE week 52
Good Friday Holiday (UK) except Scotland
Bank Holiday (Scotland) Holiday (Australia)

Saturday 30
89–276 Week 13
sr 5.42, ss 18.30
Holiday (Australia) ○ Full Moon

Sunday 31
90–275 Week 13
Easter Day

Monday **1**

91–274 Week 14

Easter Monday Holiday (UK, except Scotland)

Holiday (Republic of Ireland) Holiday (Australia)

Tuesday **2**

92–273 Week 14

Wednesday **3**

93–272 Week 14

Thursday 4
94–271 Week 14

Friday 5
95–270 Week 14 PAYE week 53

Saturday 6
96–269 Week 14 PAYE week 1
sr 5.26, ss 18.41

Sunday 7
97–268 Week 14
Low Sunday ☾ Last Quarter

Monday 8
98–267 Week 15

Tuesday 9
99–266 Week 15

Wednesday 10
100–265 Week 15

Thursday **11**
101–264 Week 15

Friday **12**
102–263 Week 15

Saturday **13**
103–262 Week 15 PAYE week 2
sr 5.11, ss 18.53

Sunday **14**
104–261 Week 15
2nd after Easter ● New Moon

Monday **15**
105–260 Week 16

Tuesday **16**
106–259 Week 16

Wednesday **17**
107–258 Week 16

Thursday **18**
108–257 Week 16

Friday **19**
109–256 Week 16

Saturday **20**
110–255 Week 16 PAYE week 3
sr 4.56, ss 19.05

Sunday **21**
111–254 Week 16
3rd after Easter ☽ First Quarter

Monday **22**
112–253 Week 17

Tuesday **23**
113–252 Week 17
St George (England)

Wednesday **24**
114–251 Week 17

Thursday 25
115–250 Week 17
Anzac Day (Australia)

Friday 26
116–249 Week 17

Saturday 27
117–248 Week 17 PAYE week 4
sr 4.41, ss 19.16

Sunday 28
118–247 Week 17
4th after Easter ○ Full Moon

Monday **29**
119–246 Week 18

Tuesday **30**
120–245 Week 18

Wednesday **May 1**
121–244 Week 18

Thursday **2**
122–243 Week 18

Friday **3**
123–242 Week 18

Saturday **4**
124–241 Week 18 PAYE week 5
sr 4.28, ss 19.28

Sunday **5**
125–240 Week 18
Rogation Sunday

Monday 6

126–239 Week 19

May Day Holiday (UK, except Scotland)

Bank Holiday (Scotland)

Tuesday 7

127–238 Week 19

☾ Last Quarter

Wednesday 8

128–237 Week 19

Thursday **9**
129–236 Week 19
Ascension Day

Friday **10**
130–235 Week 19

Saturday **11**
131–234 Week 19 PAYE week 6
sr 4.16, ss 19.39

Sunday **12**
132–233 Week 19
1st after Ascension

Monday **13**
133–232 Week 20

Tuesday **14**
134–231 Week 20
● New Moon

Wednesday **15**
135–230 Week 20
Scottish Quarter Day

Thursday **16**
136–229 Week 20

Friday **17**
137–228 Week 20

Saturday **18**
138–227 Week 20 PAYE week 7
sr 4.05, ss 19.50

Sunday **19**
139–226 Week 20
Whit Sunday

1991 **May**

Monday 20
140–225 Week 21
☽ First Quarter

Tuesday 21
141–224 Week 21

Wednesday 22
142–223 Week 21

Thursday **23**
143–222 Week 21

Friday **24**
144–221 Week 21

Saturday **25**
145–220 Week 21 PAYE week 8
sr 3.56, ss 19.59

Sunday **26**
146–219 Week 21
Trinity Sunday

Monday 27

147–218 Week 22

Spring Holiday (UK, except Scotland)

Bank Holiday (Scotland)

Tuesday 28

148–217 Week 22

○ Full Moon

Wednesday 29

149–216 Week 22

Thursday **30**
150–215 Week 22

Friday **31**
151–214 Week 22

Saturday **June 1**
152–213 Week 22 PAYE week 9
sr 3.50, ss 20.08

Sunday **2**
153–212 Week 22
1st after Trinity

Monday 3

154–211 Week 23

Holiday (Republic of Ireland)

Tuesday 4

155–210 Week 23

Wednesday 5

156–209 Week 23

☾ Last Quarter

Thursday **6**
157–208 Week 23

Friday **7**
158–207 Week 23

Saturday **8**
159–206 Week 23 PAYE week 10
sr 3.45, ss 20.15

Sunday **9**
160–205 Week 23
2nd after Trinity

Monday **10**
161–204 Week 24

Tuesday **11**
162–203 Week 24

Wednesday **12**
163–202 Week 24
● New Moon

Thursday **13**
164–201 Week 24

Friday **14**
165–200 Week 24

Saturday **15**
166–199 Week 24 PAYE week 11
sr 3.43, ss 20.19

Sunday **16**
167–198 Week 24
3rd after Trinity Fathers' Day

Monday **17**
168–197 Week 25

Tuesday **18**
169–196 Week 25

Wednesday **19**
170–195 Week 25
☽ First Quarter

Thursday **20**
171–194 Week 25

Friday **21**
172–193 Week 25
Longest Day

Saturday **22**
173–192 Week 25 PAYE week 12
sr 3.43, ss 20.22

Sunday **23**
174–191 Week 25
4th after Trinity

Monday **24**
175–190 Week 26
Midsummer Day (Quarter Day)

Tuesday **25**
176–189 Week 26

Wednesday **26**
177–188 Week 26

Thursday **27**
178–187 Week 26
○ Full Moon

Friday **28**
179–186 Week 26

Saturday **29**
180–185 Week 26 PAYE week 13
sr 3.46, ss 20.22

Sunday **30**
181–184 Week 26
5th after Trinity

Monday **1**
182–183 Week 27

Tuesday **2**
183–182 Week 27

Wednesday **3**
184–181 Week 27

Thursday **4**
185–180 Week 27

Friday **5**
186–179 Week 27
☾ Last Quarter

Saturday **6**
187–178 Week 27 PAYE week 14
sr 3.51, ss 20.19

Sunday **7**
188–177 Week 27
6th after Trinity

Monday **8**
189–176 Week 28

Tuesday **9**
190–175 Week 28

Wednesday **10**
191–174 Week 28

Thursday **11**
192–173 Week 28
● New Moon

Friday **12**
193–172 Week 28
Holiday (Northern Ireland)

Saturday **13**
194–171 Week 28 PAYE week 15
sr 3.58, ss 20.14

Sunday **14**
195–170 Week 28
7th after Trinity

Monday 15
196–169 Week 29
St Swithin

Tuesday 16
197–168 Week 29

Wednesday 17
198–167 Week 29

Thursday **18**
199–166 Week 29
☽ First Quarter

Friday **19**
200–165 Week 29

Saturday **20**
201–164 Week 29 PAYE week 16
sr 4.07, ss 20.07

Sunday **21**
202–163 Week 29
8th after Trinity

1991 July

Monday 22
203–162 Week 30

Tuesday 23
204–161 Week 30

Wednesday 24
205–160 Week 30

Thursday **25**
206–159 Week 30

Friday **26**
207–158 Week 30
○ Full Moon

Saturday **27**
208–157 Week 30 PAYE week 17
sr 4.16, ss 19.57

Sunday **28**
209–156 Week 30
9th after Trinity

Monday 29
210–155 Week 31

Tuesday 30
211–154 Week 31

Wednesday 31
212–153 Week 31

Thursday **1**
213–152 Week 31
Lammas (Scottish Quarter Day)

Friday **2**
214–151 Week 31

Saturday **3**
215–150 Week 31 PAYE week 18
sr 4.26, ss 19.46 ☾ Last Quarter

Sunday **4**
216–149 Week 31
10th after Trinity

Monday 5

217–148 Week 32

Bank Holiday (Scotland)

Holiday (Republic of Ireland)

Tuesday 6

218–147 Week 32

Wednesday 7

219–146 Week 32

Thursday **8**
220–145 Week 32

Friday **9**
221–144 Week 32

Saturday **10**
222–143 Week 32 PAYE week 19
sr 4.37, ss 19.34 ● New Moon

Sunday **11**
223–142 Week 32
11th after Trinity

Monday 12
224–141 Week 33

Tuesday 13
225–140 Week 33

Wednesday 14
226–139 Week 33

Thursday **15**
227–138 Week 33

Friday **16**
228–137 Week 33

Saturday **17**
229–136 Week 33 PAYE week 20
sr 4.48, ss 19.20 ☽ First Quarter

Sunday **18**
230–135 Week 33
12th after Trinity

Monday 19
231–134 Week 34

Tuesday 20
232–133 Week 34

Wednesday 21
233–132 Week 34

Thursday **22**
234–131 Week 34

Friday **23**
235–130 Week 34

Saturday **24**
236–129 Week 34 PAYE week 21
sr 4.59, ss 19.06

Sunday **25**
237–128 Week 34
13th after Trinity ○ Full Moon

Monday **26**
238–127 Week 35
Late Summer Holiday (UK, except Scotland)

Tuesday **27**
239–126 Week 35

Wednesday **28**
240–125 Week 35

Thursday **29**
241–124 Week 35

Friday **30**
242–123 Week 35

Saturday **31**
243–122 Week 35 PAYE week 22
sr 5.11, ss 18.51

Sunday **September 1**
244–121 Week 35
14th after Trinity ☾ Last Quarter

Monday 2
245–120 Week 36

Tuesday 3
246–119 Week 36

Wednesday 4
247–118 Week 36

Thursday **5**
248–117 Week 36

Friday **6**
249–116 Week 36

Saturday **7**
250–115 Week 36 PAYE week 23
sr 5.22, ss 18.35

Sunday **8**
251–114 Week 36
15th after Trinity ● New Moon

1991 September

Monday **9**
252–113 Week 37

Tuesday **10**
253–112 Week 37

Wednesday **11**
254–111 Week 37

Thursday **12**
255–110 Week 37

Friday **13**
256–109 Week 37

Saturday **14**
257–108 Week 37 PAYE week 24
sr 5.33, ss 18.19

Sunday **15**
258–107 Week 37
16th after Trinity ☽ First Quarter

1991 September

Monday 16
259–106 Week 38

Tuesday 17
260–105 Week 38

Wednesday 18
261–104 Week 38

Thursday **19**
262–103 Week 38

Friday **20**
263–102 Week 38

Saturday **21**
264–101 Week 38 PAYE week 25
sr 5.44, ss 18.03

Sunday **22**
265–100 Week 38
17th after Trinity

1991 September

Monday 23

266–99 Week 39

Autumnal Equinox ○ Full Moon

Tuesday 24

267–98 Week 39

Wednesday 25

268–97 Week 39

Thursday **26**
269–96 Week 39

Friday **27**
270–95 Week 39

Saturday **28**
271–94 Week 39 PAYE week 26
sr 5.55, ss 17.47

Sunday **29**
272–93 Week 39
18th after Trinity Michaelmas Day (Quarter Day)

1991 **September**

Monday **30**

273–92 Week 40

Tuesday **October** **1**

274–91 Week 40

☾ Last Quarter

Wednesday **2**

275–90 Week 40

Thursday **3**
276–89 Week 40

Friday **4**
277–88 Week 40

Saturday **5**
278–87 Week 40 PAYE week 27
sr 6.07, ss 17.31

Sunday **6**
279–86 Week 40
19th after Trinity

Monday **7**

280–85 Week 41

● New Moon

Tuesday **8**

281–84 Week 41

Wednesday **9**

282–83 Week 41

Thursday **10**
283–82 Week 41

Friday **11**
284–81 Week 41

Saturday **12**
285–80 Week 41 PAYE week 28
sr 6.19, ss 17.15

Sunday **13**
286–79 Week 41
20th after Trinity

1991 **October**

Monday **14**

287–78 Week 42

Tuesday **15**

288–77 Week 42

☽ First Quarter

Wednesday **16**

289–76 Week 42

Thursday **17**
290–75 Week 42

Friday **18**
291–74 Week 42

Saturday **19**
292–73 Week 42 PAYE week 29
sr 6.31, ss 17.00

Sunday **20**
293–72 Week 42
21st after Trinity

1991 October

Monday **21**
294–71 Week 43

Tuesday **22**
295–70 Week 43

Wednesday **23**
296–69 Week 43
○ Full Moon

Thursday **24**
297–68 Week 43

Friday **25**
298–67 Week 43

Saturday **26**
299–66 Week 43 PAYE week 30
sr 6.43, ss 16.46

Sunday **27**
300–65 Week 43
22nd after Trinity

Monday **28**
301–64 Week 44
Holiday (Republic of Ireland)

Tuesday **29**
302–63 Week 44

Wednesday **30**
303–62 Week 44
☾ Last Quarter

Thursday **31**
304–61 Week 44
Hallowe'en

Friday **November** **1**
305–60 Week 44

Saturday **2**
306–59 Week 44 PAYE week 31
sr 6.55, ss 16.33

Sunday **3**
307–58 Week 44
23rd after Trinity

Monday **4**
308–57 Week 45

Tuesday **5**
309–56 Week 45

Wednesday **6**
310–55 Week 45
● New Moon

Thursday **7**
311–54 Week 45

Friday **8**
312–53 Week 45

Saturday **9**
313–52 Week 45 PAYE week 32
sr 7.07, ss 16.21

Sunday **10**
314–51 Week 45
24th after Trinity Remembrance Sunday

1991 November

Monday **11**

315–50 Week 46

Martinmas (Scottish Quarter Day)

Tuesday **12**

316–49 Week 46

Wednesday **13**

317–48 Week 46

Thursday **14**
318–47 Week 46
☽ First Quarter

Friday **15**
319–46 Week 46

Saturday **16**
320–45 Week 46 PAYE week 33
sr 7.19, ss 16.11

Sunday **17**
321–44 Week 46
25th after Trinity

Monday 18
322–43 Week 47

Tuesday 19
323–42 Week 47

Wednesday 20
324–41 Week 47

Thursday **21**
325–40 Week 47
○ Full Moon

Friday **22**
326–39 Week 47

Saturday **23**
327–38 Week 47 PAYE week 34
sr 7.31, ss 16.02

Sunday **24**
328–37 Week 47
26th after Trinity

1991 November

Monday **25**

329–36 Week 48

Tuesday **26**

330–35 Week 48

Wednesday **27**

331–34 Week 48

Thursday **28**
332–33 Week 48
☾ Last Quarter

Friday **29**
333–32 Week 48

Saturday **30**
334–31 Week 48 PAYE week 35
St Andrew (Scotland) sr 7.42, ss 15.56

Sunday **December** **1**
335–30 Week 48
1st in Advent

Monday **2**

336–29 Week 49

Tuesday **3**

337–28 Week 49

Wednesday **4**

338–27 Week 49

Thursday **5**
339–26 Week 49

Friday **6**
340–25 Week 49
● New Moon

Saturday **7**
341–24 Week 49 PAYE week 36
sr 7.51, ss 15.53

Sunday **8**
342–23 Week 49
2nd in Advent

Monday **9**
343–22 Week 50

Tuesday **10**
344–21 Week 50

Wednesday **11**
345–20 Week 50

Thursday **12**
346–19 Week 50

Friday **13**
347–18 Week 50

Saturday **14**
348–17 Week 50 PAYE week 37
sr 7.59, ss 15.52 ☽ First Quarter

Sunday **15**
349–16 Week 50
3rd in Advent

Monday **16**
350–15 Week 51

Tuesday **17**
351–14 Week 51

Wednesday **18**
352–13 Week 51

Thursday **19**
353–12 Week 51

Friday **20**
354–11 Week 51

Saturday **21**
355–10 Week 51 PAYE week 38
sr 8.04, ss 15.53 ○ Full Moon

Sunday **22**
356–9 Week 51
4th in Advent Shortest Day

Monday **23**
357–8 Week 52

Tuesday **24**
358–7 Week 52

Wednesday **25**
359–6 Week 52 Christmas Day (Quarter Day)
Holiday (UK and Republic of Ireland) Holiday (Australia)

Thursday **26**
360–5 Week 52 Boxing Day
Holiday (UK, except Scotland) Bank Holiday (Scotland)
Holiday (Republic of Ireland) Holiday (Australia)

Friday **27**
361–4 Week 52

Saturday **28**
362–3 Week 52 PAYE week 39
sr 8.06, ss 15.58 ☾ Last Quarter

Sunday **29**
363–2 Week 52
1st after Christmas

Monday **30**
364–1 Week 1

Tuesday **31**
365–0 Week 1

Wednesday **January 1992** **1**
1–365 Week 1
New Year's Day Holiday (UK)
Holiday (Republic of Ireland) Holiday (Australia)

Thursday **2**
2–364 Week 1
Bank Holiday (Scotland)

Friday **3**
3–363 Week 1

Saturday **4**
4–362 Week 1 PAYE week 40
sr 8.06, ss 16.05 ● New Moon

Sunday **5**
5–361 Week 1
2nd after Christmas

1992 Forward Planner

January	February	March
1 W	1 S	1 S
2 T	2 S	2 M
3 F	3 M	3 T
4 S	4 T	4 W
5 S	5 W	5 T
6 M	6 T	6 F
7 T	7 F	7 S
8 W	8 S	8 S
9 T	9 S	9 M
10 F	10 M	10 T
11 S	11 T	11 W
12 S	12 W	12 T
13 M	13 T	13 F
14 T	14 F	14 S
15 W	15 S	15 S
16 T	16 S	16 M
17 F	17 M	17 T
18 S	18 T	18 W
19 S	19 W	19 T
20 M	20 T	20 F
21 T	21 F	21 S
22 W	22 S	22 S
23 T	23 S	23 M
24 F	24 M	24 T
25 S	25 T	25 W
26 S	26 W	26 T
27 M	27 T	27 F
28 T	28 F	28 S
29 W	29 S	29 S
30 T		30 M
31 F		31 T

1992 Forward Planner

April	May	June
1 W	1 F	1 M
2 T	2 S	2 T
3 F	3 [S]	3 W
4 S	4 M	4 T
5 [S]	5 T	5 F
6 M	6 W	6 S
7 T	7 T	7 [S]
8 W	8 F	8 M
9 T	9 S	9 T
10 F	10 [S]	10 W
11 S	11 M	11 T
12 [S]	12 T	12 F
13 M	13 W	13 S
14 T	14 T	14 [S]
15 W	15 F	15 M
16 T	16 S	16 T
17 F	17 [S]	17 W
18 S	18 M	18 T
19 [S]	19 T	19 F
20 M	20 W	20 S
21 T	21 T	21 [S]
22 W	22 F	22 M
23 T	23 S	23 T
24 F	24 [S]	24 W
25 S	25 M	25 T
26 [S]	26 T	26 F
27 M	27 W	27 S
28 T	28 T	28 [S]
29 W	29 F	29 M
30 T	30 S	30 T
	31 [S]	

1992 Forward Planner

July	August	September
1 W	1 S	1 T
2 T	2 [S]	2 W
3 F	3 M	3 T
4 S	4 T	4 F
5 [S]	5 W	5 S
6 M	6 T	6 [S]
7 T	7 F	7 M
8 W	8 S	8 T
9 T	9 [S]	9 W
10 F	10 M	10 T
11 S	11 T	11 F
12 [S]	12 W	12 S
13 M	13 T	13 [S]
14 T	14 F	14 M
15 W	15 S	15 T
16 T	16 [S]	16 W
17 F	17 M	17 T
18 S	18 T	18 F
19 [S]	19 W	19 S
20 M	20 T	20 [S]
21 T	21 F	21 M
22 W	22 S	22 T
23 T	23 [S]	23 W
24 F	24 M	24 T
25 S	25 T	25 F
26 [S]	26 W	26 S
27 M	27 T	27 [S]
28 T	28 F	28 M
29 W	29 S	29 T
30 T	30 [S]	30 W
31 F	31 M	

1992 Forward Planner

October	November	December
1 T	1 S	1 T
2 F	2 M	2 W
3 S	3 T	3 T
4 S	4 W	4 F
5 M	5 T	5 S
6 T	6 F	6 S
7 W	7 S	7 M
8 T	8 S	8 T
9 F	9 M	9 W
10 S	10 T	10 T
11 S	11 W	11 F
12 M	12 T	12 S
13 T	13 F	13 S
14 W	14 S	14 M
15 T	15 S	15 T
16 F	16 M	16 W
17 S	17 T	17 T
18 S	18 W	18 F
19 M	19 T	19 S
20 T	20 F	20 S
21 W	21 S	21 M
22 T	22 S	22 T
23 F	23 M	23 W
24 S	24 T	24 T
25 S	25 W	25 F
26 M	26 T	26 S
27 T	27 F	27 S
28 W	28 S	28 M
29 T	29 S	29 T
30 F	30 M	30 W
31 S		31 T

Notes

Notes

Notes

Notes

Cash Account

January

Debit

Total

Credit

Total

February

Cash Account

Debit

Total

Credit

Total

Cash Account

March

Debit

Total

Credit

Total

Cash Account

Debit

Total

Credit

Total

Cash Account

May

Debit			
Total			

Credit			
Total			

June

Cash Account

Debit

Total

Credit

Total

Cash Account

July

Debit

Total

Credit

Total

August

Cash Account

Debit

Total

Credit

Total

Cash Account

September

Debit			

Total

Credit			

Total

October

Cash Account

Debit

Total

Credit

Total

Cash Account

November

Debit

Total

Credit

Total

December

Cash Account

Debit

Total

Credit

Total

Annual Cash Summary 1991

	Debit		Credit	
Balance brought forward				
January				
February				
March				
April				
May				
June				
July				
August				
September				
October				
November				
December				
Total				
Balance carried forward				

Design: W M de Majo MBE FSIAD Made in Great Britain